NUCLEAR FACTS

NUCLEAR FACTS

Christy Campbell

HAMLYN

LONDON · NEW YORK · SYDNEY · TORONTO

Designed by Sue Rawkins for Campbell Rawkins

Cover Photography: Tony Stone
Illustrations: Hayward Art Group

First published in 1984 by
The Hamlyn Publishing Group Limited
London · New York · Sydney · Toronto
Astronaut House, Feltham, Middlesex, England

© Copyright The Hamlyn Publishing Group Limited 1984

ISBN 0 600 38522 1

Printed in Italy

Contents

Introduction

This is a book of information and not of opinion. Its subject matter is weapons of mass destruction, the plans for their use, the strategy behind those plans and the means of carrying them out. That is an agenda which stirs the most fundamental of feelings and sets passionate pens to paper—but not here.

By its nature it is concerned only marginally with the effects of nuclear weapons on life and the things that support life. Nor is it concerned in any degree with attempts to survive the impact of the megatons by digging holes or seeking places of safety.

It is in fact made up of dispassionate commentary on weapons systems and the command structures that seek to control them. The diagrams that explain how a given weapons system works are drawn from material provided by manufacturers and project-system offices and have the same detachment as their originals. If such clinical analysis of a subject like this is repellent to some, it should be made clear that it is only by entering the culture of the technology, however reluctantly, that the politics of nuclear weapons be understood, because the technologists so often lead the policy-makers by the nose.

The nature of delivery systems that can fly between continents in tens of minutes and annihilate the political command structure of an opponent means that the luxury of time for reflection is excluded from decision taking. The government of a nuclear-armed state does not have to persuade its citizens to *fight* a nuclear war—that is not their decision, nor can it be if deterrence is to be believable. It has to persuade its citizens to *prepare* for nuclear war and keep those preparations at the highest state of technical competence and readiness. The piling up of massive nuclear arsenals becomes a background activity in peace-time—a routine, if highly secretive, aspect of government, whether in a democracy or in the closed command society of the Soviet Union.

There are factors within the culture of nuclear weapons technology which continually push the size of the stockpiles ever higher and these factors must be understood if the momentum is to be reversed. Why, for example, did the number of individually triggered nuclear devices climb at an exponential rate in parallel with the fluctuating process of detente? Why did nuclear weapons change from war-terminating city smashers to war-fighting sniper's rifles, capable of 'taking out' a critical, pinpointed target over a range of thousands of kilometres? Why does Europe (as much more volatile flashpoints soon will) bristle with tactical nuclear weapons, which even the men who command them now regard as a deadly self-made booby trap? The answer lies in technology, not policy.

The nuclear stockpile of the United States has an estimated explosive yield approximating to 9000 million tons of TNT and the Soviet stockpile can be considered, in crude terms, its equal in destructive capacity. This represents the equivalent of two Hiroshima bombs joining the arsenals of the super-powers every half hour, day and night, for nearly 40 years and that pace is about to quicken. Britain, France and China wave their smaller nuclear bludgeons on the sidelines and each has plans to dramatically increase their potential.

Meanwhile, because of more than 35 years of surly constancy in the fundamental relations between the superpowers, the unbroken threat of annihilation has been taken for granted. Life, commerce, international relations and a fitful diplomacy continue, while the tensions created by ideological confrontation are discharged in proxy wars in the Third World, in the electronic intelligence duel, in shadow-box rehearsals for mass conventional war in Europe or the Middle East, and even in the shooting down of civilian airliners.

The story of nuclear weapons and nuclear strategies contained in this book is, therefore, concerned not with real events but with the minutiae of military technology and with the plans for the use of the resulting weapons systems. By their nature both strive to ensure their own futility. For this there are no apologies.

1
The
Nuclear
Web

Atomic weapons and invulnerable delivery systems came of age together. The last V-2 ballistic rocket, against which there was no defence other than the destruction of its bases, fell on London four months before a US Army Air Force B-29 dropped 'Little Boy' on Hiroshima. One thousand and fifty-four V-2s tipped with a ton of high explosive each fell on London and killed 9277 people. Two bombs on two Japanese cities killed over a quarter of a million.

The atom bomb is a weapon. A missile or a bomber is a delivery system. In the 1950s thermonuclear weapons or H-bombs were developed with explosive power far greater than the atom bombs of 1945. The biggest ever known to have been tested, by the Soviet Union in 1962, exploded with a force of 3000 Hiroshima bombs. However, the military imperative has in fact been to make nuclear weapons even *smaller*, providing explosive yields appropriate to a given requirement, whether it is an area-defence, anti-aircraft missile or a device to destroy cities. With the weapon itself made compact, reliable and deadly, the delivery system becomes critical, that is, the aircraft or missile which carries the warhead, as do its own factors of reliability, accuracy, ability to get through and, very important, its capacity to survive either when over the target or at its own base under an equivalent attack.

Nuclear fission is the splitting of the nuclei of heavy atoms such as uranium or plutonium. Nuclear fusion is the combination of light atoms such as hydrogen isotopes. In both processes part of the mass of these elements is converted into energy and, if this can be made to happen fast enough, a nuclear explosion is the result. The atomic bomb relied on fission for its power, whereas thermonuclear weapons work by fusion.

The atomic bombs constructed so far have used the isotopes uranium 235 or plutonium 239 as the fissile material. To trigger a fission reaction it is necessary to put together a mass of these materials large enough to ensure that the high-energy neutron particles inside do not escape from the surface of the mass but strike other heavy atoms within the material, causing them in turn to release more neutrons and set up a chain-reaction. The smallest amount of material which will do this is called the critical mass. This in turn depends on the purity and density of the material and its physical environment. If the material is surrounded by a reflective medium, such as pure uranium, more neutrons are bounced back into the material, reducing its critical mass.

The critical mass of weapons-grade plutonium 239 is around 10 kg and, if the plutonium sphere were surrounded by a reflector, it would come down to under 5 kg, just 7 cm across. This mass has first to be brought together and then held long enough for a fission chain-reaction to occur or to prevent a chain-reaction starting before maximum supercriticality is reached (pre-initiation). The Hiroshima bomb fired two slugs of uranium into each other, using high explosive. The Nagasaki bomb used high-explosive lenses arranged around a hollow sphere of plutonium to compress its subcritical mass into supercriticality, with a neutron-producing 'initiator' of polonium and beryllium inside. The neutron pulse was fired as the plutonium was compressed inwards. The 20-kiloton explosion that destroyed Nagasaki was the result. The maximum explosive yield of atomic-fission weapons is limited to a scale of kilotons by the factor of critical mass. However, the very high energies generated by a fission weapon are enough to trigger its opposite, the fusion of light atoms into heavier ones. In thermonuclear weapons the heavier isotopes of hydrogen, deuterium and tritium are fused into helium. In order to make it work, temperatures above 100 million °C are required to impart enough energy to the component nuclei to overcome the positive-positive repulsion between them. However, since no critical mass is involved, in theory there is no limit to the yield of fusion or thermonuclear weapons.

A fission trigger is used to create these tremendous energies which must be delivered to the fusion material in a space of time much shorter than it takes for the explosion to occur, in fact with a speed approaching that of light. This factor makes the design and manufacture of fusion weapons much more problematic than those of fission weapons.

The effective destructive power of any weapon is a function of accuracy of delivery, reliability and energy yield. The energy yield of nuclear weapons is expressed as the equivalent weight of TNT that would have to be exploded in one place to produce the same effects. A one-megaton (one million tons of TNT) warhead does not have destructive effects a thousand times greater than those produced by a single kiloton (1000 tons). The area of destruction increases by the cube root of the yield; thus, many smaller weapons spread their effects over a wider area than a single very large weapon.

The effects of nuclear weapons

The immediate effects of a nuclear explosion are blast, heat and ionizing radiation in proportions depending on the type of weapon and where it was exploded – in the air, under ground or under water, for example. In a standard case roughly half the energy would be released as blast, a third as heat and the remainder as radiation, both 'prompt' in the initial detonation and long-term as fallout.

The flash of heat comes first. X-rays from the explosion are absorbed by the surrounding air and progressively re-radiated on longer wavelengths. The process leads to the formation of a luminous mass of air, the 'fireball', which grows and rises. In a one-megaton burst the radius of the fireball at maximum

The awesome terror of a thermonuclear explosion revealed in a French atmospheric test at Mururoa atoll in the South Pacific. After international protest France ceased atmospheric tests in 1974. The last such test was by China in 1980.

Fallout: The way the wind blows

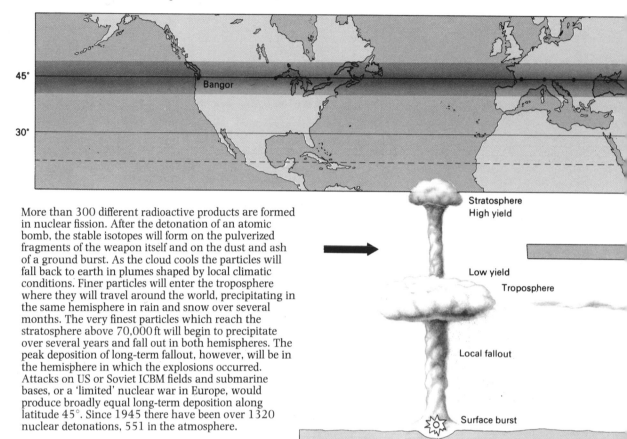

More than 300 different radioactive products are formed in nuclear fission. After the detonation of an atomic bomb, the stable isotopes will form on the pulverized fragments of the weapon itself and on the dust and ash of a ground burst. As the cloud cools the particles will fall back to earth in plumes shaped by local climatic conditions. Finer particles will enter the troposphere where they will travel around the world, precipitating in the same hemisphere in rain and snow over several months. The very finest particles which reach the stratosphere above 70,000 ft will begin to precipitate over several years and fall out in both hemispheres. The peak deposition of long-term fallout, however, will be in the hemisphere in which the explosions occurred. Attacks on US or Soviet ICBM fields and submarine bases, or a 'limited' nuclear war in Europe, would produce broadly equal long-term deposition along latitude 45°. Since 1945 there have been over 1320 nuclear detonations, 551 in the atmosphere.

intensity is 1200 m. The heat flash is not so effective against dispersed military targets, such as armour or hardened missile silos, but against cities dense with human beings the effect is devastating. The fireball will sear the flesh of people in the open, and dry-roast or asphyxiate those in deep shelters. If the fireball touches the ground a crater will be gouged out, with everything within it vaporized. It is estimated that a ten-megaton air burst could produce retinal burns in survivors who glanced at the flash at a distance more than 90 mi. from ground zero.

A city ripped open by the blast will begin to burn and, under certain conditions, the many fires will merge to create a convective column of hot, rising gas. This will produce winds whipping into the base of the chimney, pulling in more oxygen and fuelling the debris, with temperatures rising to 1000°C. The resulting firestorm would only happen under certain climatic conditions, such as those present during the RAF Bomber Command attack on Hamburg in 1943. There was no firestorm at Nagasaki.

Blast comes next, carrying half the weapon's total energy, and its effects are conditioned by the height of the burst. In an airburst at medium height the blast front extends out in two spheres from the point of detonation and in an echo from the ground, merging into a so-called mach front, which may have a peak over pressure of almost twice that of the original blast front. Behind the blast front is an area of pressure below that of the atmosphere, and winds travelling at several hundred miles an hour will accompany the effects. The human body can stand up to twice the normal atmospheric pressure, but an 'overpressure' of 0.5 lb per square inch (psi) will shatter glass. Ten psi is the standard for calculating a lethal area for blast effects and in a one-megaton airburst 300 m high the lethal distance is nearly 5 km. Much more dangerous to flesh and blood are the masonry and glass shards whipped up by the winds and strewn around with all the deadly effects of a cluster bomb, but to far greater distances.

Radiation and fallout

Various types of weapons and conditions produce different mixes of radiation—neutrons, X-rays, gamma-rays, alpha and beta particles. Dose for dose, neutrons are more dangerous to the human body but do not travel as far as gamma rays. The amount of

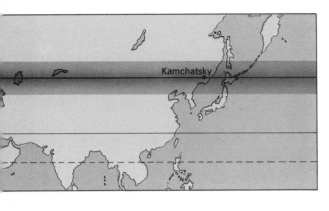

Prevailing winds

Precipitation in rain

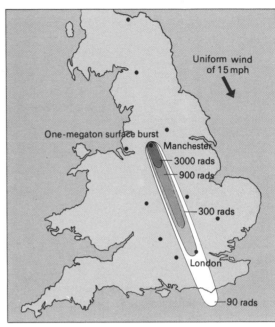

The fallout pattern assuming a one-megaton surface burst on Manchester, the plume shaped by a uniform north-westerly wind of 15 mph. An equivalent south-easterly wind would engulf Edinburgh. The contours indicate accumulated doses of 3000, 900, 300 and 90 rads to unprotected people. A dose of 450–500 rads will kill about half of those exposed to it.

gamma radiation falls off according to the square of the distance from the source, combined with the absorption effects of the material through which it travels. As a blast wave moves outwards, the air density behind the front is lowered and the gamma rays travelling through it are less attenuated. However, the effects of radiation fall off with distance much faster than the other effects—a one-megaton thermonuclear weapon would produce a dose of 200,000 rads at a slant distance of 1 km. At 2 km that has fallen to 700 rads, bearing in mind that a total tissue surface dose of 4500 rads would be lethal to 50% of healthy adults.

But this lethal radius is the same as that for blast and heat effects—people in the way of a one-megaton bomb will be killed three times over. For smaller weapons the reverse is true: the ratio of radiation to blast and heat becomes greater and this is the principle behind the so-called neutron bomb.

The amount of neutron radiation can be enhanced by other engineering means. When the power is so small that lethal radiation (which may not kill a tank crew behind armour plate immediately) is greater than the lethal blast and heat radius, the overall area affected is down to around 2 km in radius.

A nuclear explosion will release a range of radioactive isotopes, from the products of its own fission, from radioactivity induced by neutron bombardment of the weapons materials, from the plutonium and uranium which did not undergo fission and the tritium from fusion reactions. Altogether some 300 different radioactive products are formed in fission, with half-lives ranging from a fraction of a second to millions of years. The half-life of a radioactive substance is the time required for the level of radioactivity to decay by 50%. But, in spite of this complexity, as a general rule, after a nuclear explosion the radiation dose will decay according to the formula $t^{-1.2}$ where t equals time. This means that the level of radioactivity will decline by ten for every sevenfold elapse in time.

Meanwhile the blast and heat will have pulverized the target, reducing it to a rising hot cloud of dust and ash. As the cloud cools the stable fission isotopes begin to form on the particles, falling back to earth relatively quickly in cigar-shaped plumes, according to wind direction, while rain will produce local hot spots. The very finest particles are carried up high into the atmosphere. Those that enter the troposphere will travel around the world in about 12 days and will stay largely in the same hemisphere, precipitating in rain and snow over several months. However, the bulk of the particles will be confined to a relatively narrow band centred on the target areas. The more gradual the descent, the less the radioactivity, since more will have decayed before reaching the ground.

The very finest particles that reach the stratosphere above 70,000 feet will begin to precipitate after several years and will be fairly evenly distributed between the hemispheres, but the largest part of overall long-term fallout will tend to come down in the hemisphere where the explosions occurred. Assuming a war involving the United States and the Soviet Union, or a so-called 'limited' nuclear war in Europe, the peak deposition would be on latitude 45°, running through the northern United States, south-central Europe, the southern Soviet Union and Japan. Thus, the inhabitants of Bordeaux would receive the same amount of long-term fallout from detonations over the US Navy's Strategic Weapons Facility, Pacific, at Bangor, near Bremerton Naval Base, or over the Soviet Union missile submarine base at Kamchatsky on the Pacific. The amount of persistence of stratospheric fallout again depends on weather and climatic conditions.

Because the short-lived nuclides will have decayed, the danger from global fallout is brought about by the ingestion of radioactive materials or through a food-chain. Caesium 137 enters through fish and vegetables and admits gamma rays as it decays. Strontium-90 enters through a food-chain from grass to animals to milk and meat, and builds up in bones and teeth.

Whatever the kind of radiation from fallout, prompt or residual, the injury to biological tissue is produced by electrons already in the tissue absorbing energy from the incoming radiation. The consequences for the individual cells depend on the energy received by the cell's sensitive components, the nucleus and the genetic material, the chromosomes and genes. The tissues most sensitive are lymphoid tissue, bone marrow, spleen, male testes and the gastrointestinal tract. The higher the dose, the greater the damage, but if exposure is spread over weeks or more the body can tolerate higher doses, because cellular recovery is taking place while irradiation continues. Animals will be similarly affected, while the ability for crop seeds to germinate may be destroyed and crops grown on contaminated soil will build up the longer-lived isotopes. Hard-bodied insects, bacteria, fungi and viruses are highly resistant to radiation and they could be expected to proliferate in a fecund environment of unburied corpses and unpurified water.

Apart from fallout, the great conflagration of cities and vast forest fires would produce a darkening aerosol in the atmosphere, affecting its dynamics. The destruction of nuclear power stations, storage sites,

The Boeing E-4B National Airborne Command Post which would carry the President of the United States or his successors aloft to ride out a nuclear attack.

reprocessing centres and nuclear-powered warships would bleed more long-lived nuclear compounds into the soil and seas. The collapse of medical and economic structures would expose the survivors to starvation, disease and psychological agony. In the first two weeks there would be a glut of chicken stew from the slaughtered products of battery farms. Every mouthful, and every cup of water would mean the ingestion of more contaminated material to irradiate the body from within.

Weapons systems

Nuclear weapons are ideal devices for destroying human life and the things that support life on a mass scale. This ironically makes them less rather than more militarily 'useful'.

Military considerations do not recognize 'over-kill'—that is, the allocation of an amount of explosive

power per head of the population. Military considerations are about targets which, while they may be cities dense with human beings, are also missile silos and underground command centres. City smashing is what 'mutual assured destruction' was all about and it remained the policy of the United States for a long time (*see* page 33). In the early 1970s, however, new technologies opened up an alternative to the hostage city strategy. The technological change was in the accuracy of delivery systems and the new alternative was called 'counterforce'.

Counterforce is a new word for an old military idea. It meant attacking the weapons of your opponent, not his social structure or his long-term means to make war, such as factories or power stations ('countervalue'). During the Second World War there were notable counterforce attacks, such as those by the Luftwaffe on RAF Fighter Command's airfields in 1940 or the Japanese Navy Air Force attack on the US fleet at Pearl Harbor in 1941. Countervalue attacks, such as area bombing of cities in an attempt to break a

nation's will to make war, were far less effective than attacks on military economic targets such as oil hydrogenation plants or precision tool centres.

In terms of nuclear weapons, counterforce targeting policy is only relevant in a first strike. A Soviet strike on the United States would only invite response by the surviving counterforce weapons on empty missile silos and deserted bomber bases. The policy further undermines the structure of deterrence by opening up 'war-fighting' strategies, with winners and losers.

In order to destroy a 'hardened' military target, sufficient blast overpressure must be created to root out thousands of tons of ferroconcrete. This may mean using more than one warhead but the key is accuracy of delivery and accuracy in fixing the target's real position. The accuracy of any weapon can be measured in terms of the radius of a target-centred circle, within which half the warheads from such a delivery system will fall. This is called the 'circular error probable' or CEP. If the gyro guidance

Site III of the US Ballistic Missile Early Warning System (BMEWS) on Fylingdales Moor, Yorkshire, in England. Very large tracking radars peer across the Arctic Circle waiting for the first glimmer of a Soviet ICBM arcing through space.

system of a V-2 had been used at intercontinental range the CEP would have been more than 50 miles. The MX Peacekeeper missile has been quoted with a CEP of 250 metres.

The flight of a missile from launch point to impact is a matter of mathematics. The basis of missile guidance is inertial navigation, an assembly of gyroscopes which stabilize a set of acceleromotors, recording every change in speed and direction. By knowing where it started and building in a time factor a computer can process information in order to give the missile steering commands, while satellite mapping will predict the real position of a given point of impact.

The system can be further refined. The Trident II submarine-launched missile will employ stellar inertial navigation. This involves taking mid-flight star shots which are compared with a map held in the missile's computer. Increasing the accuracy of submarine-based missiles makes them 'counterforce capable', whereas the first generation (such as the Royal Navy's Polaris A3) were only suitable for area targets.

With precision equipment being hurled around at enormous speeds, reliability is a vital factor. The reliability of Soviet systems is rated at 80%, those of the United States a little higher. Ability to penetrate defences is another consideration.

An intercontinental ballistic missile is a space rocket. It uses chemical energy in its boost phase to propel its payload into the required ballistic trajectory like the shell from a gun. Unlike a shell, however, the payload can be a small spacecraft with its own guidance and motors to make course corrections. This post-boost vehicle (PBV) can carry individual re-entry vehicles, each containing a nuclear weapon, and deliver them so that they fall in a required pattern or 'footprint'. Thus, missiles can fly between continents and release a swarm of individual MIRVs which can obliterate multiple targets. In short, they can be aimed not just at cities or sprawling oil refineries. They can attack the rival ICBMs in their silos.

Minuteman silos have a carapace of concrete hardened up to 2500 psi, the amount of blast overpressure needed to destroy them. Submarines, because they operate at ocean depths, are hardened to around 1000 psi, although close underwater bursts will fracture their internal systems. SALT I prohibited size increase in silos in excess of 32% and Pentagon studies showed that doubling the hardening of Minuteman silos would mean a fourfold increase in dimensions.

Thus, it is possible, given the CEP, the overpressure at impact, the reliability factor and the estimated hardness of the target, to calculate the amount of force necessary to smash the opponent's fixed-site weapons. This is sometimes expressed as 'counter-military potential' or CMP.

The huge increase in the Soviet Union's ICBM force in the 1970s particularly alarmed US planners. With the technology of the time, land-based ICBMs were more accurate and had a far greater 'throw weight' than sea-based missiles. This is what the 'window of vulnerability (*see* page 52) protagonists were so alarmed about and why the search for a basing-system for the MX Peacekeeper missile was of far greater political importance than what it would do at the other end.

Command and control

The new fact of counterforce has had another result. The weapons in their silos might be vulnerable but just as dangerous was the threat to the command, control and communications ('C-cubed' or 'C³') networks, which would at least ensure that messages from the national command authority or its surviving designated successors would be able to order retaliation. There is a corollary which has little to do with deterrence. As counterforce opens up 'warfighting' potential and strategies for 'a prolonged nuclear war' (*see* page 53) are openly discussed, the emphasis on giving C³ networks the capacity to survive becomes correspondingly intensified.

Modern war and modern weapons are designed to bring together a sequence of preplanned and automated events, concentrating deadly force in time and place. This is true whether the weapon is an anti-ship missile or a nuclear warhead, and the whole depends on an interlocking command and control network which informs and animates the components, while the weapons themselves depend on electronics for their individual concentrations of destructive power. Electronic warfare is concerned to protect this structure or to disrupt or destroy it. This concept can be developed from a cloud of metal filings strewn in the path of a missile's radar seeker to an attempt to destroy the decision-making head or isolate it from the force it is commanding — sometimes called 'decapitation'.

The existence of weapons of mass destruction which can fly between continents in a few minutes allows only a brief time for the decision-making process. There can be no testing of the national will to make war or recruiting and gathering of great armies as in previous 'total' wars. Whether for democracy or dictatorship the decision making is concentrated at the very top, working through military command structures in order to get the weapons of retaliation on their way to predesignated targets within minutes. The efficiency and survival capacity of command and control structures are therefore as vital a component of strategic nuclear forces as the weapons themselves. What is even more important is the ability of the political decision-making head to survive before the military command structure locks in with its predetermined plans. But, ironically, as the technology of C³ has expanded into critical computer nodes and space-based satellite relays so has the accuracy and destructive power of the weapons it controls. It is calculated, for example, that two massive Soviet SS-18 ICBMs could crush even Cheyenne Mountain (Colorado), from under which NORAD controls the missile watch on the United States. Similarly, a proportion of US Army Pershing II ballistic missiles are fitted with earth-penetrator front ends to take their thermonuclear warheads deep underground before they explode. Published figures indicate that they would fall 12% short of command centres around Moscow, a range they could cover in a matter of minutes from a launch in southern West Germany. That shortfall in range is a small challenge to a systems engineer.

The counterforce threat to earthbound command centres invites strategies which have even less time for political decision making. One is called 'launch on warning', which means relying on electronic indications that an attack is inbound. The second, 'launch under attack', is self-explanatory. The last line of defence against decapitation is waiting in 50 Minuteman II silos at Whiteman AFB, Missouri. This Emergency Rocket Communication System (ERCS) carries satellites which will beam out universal launch orders to surviving ballistic-missile submarines. Once launched they cannot be recalled.

Overall control of the US armed forces is vested in the National Command Authority (NCA), with the President at its head. In the event of the incapacity or inaccessibility of the President, the authority to order the launch of nuclear weapons passes from Vice-President to Defense Secretary, to Deputy Defense Secretary, to Chairman of the Joint Chiefs of Staff and down to the USAF major-general who is duty commander aboard the SAC airborne command post, the lowest-ranking officer in possession of the nuclear codes. At all times the President is accompanied by a military officer carrying the 'football', containing the randomly generated number sequences which are the 'go codes' for various nuclear launch orders. When President Reagan was shot and wounded in March 1981, the football was lost for 36 hours. Vice-President Bush was aboard an aircraft without full C³ facilities, so the nuclear mantle passed to the Defense Secretary, Caspar Weinberger, who had to rapidly disabuse the Secretary of State, Alexander Haig, of the idea that he (Haig) was in charge at the White House. Weinberger raised the readiness of the US forces from five to four on the five-point scale of condition of readiness.

The building of a national military command system for nuclear forces began in the 1950s. The effort was intensified when John F. Kennedy became President, since the deterrent concepts of his new Secretary of Defense, Robert McNamara, required a much finer touch on the controls and many more options than before. The first EC-135 Looking Glass flying command posts for the Strategic Air Command were airborne in Feb. 1961. After the Cuba missile crisis, more aircraft were assigned, making a total of 31, including tankers and one aircraft allocated to the President and his staff.

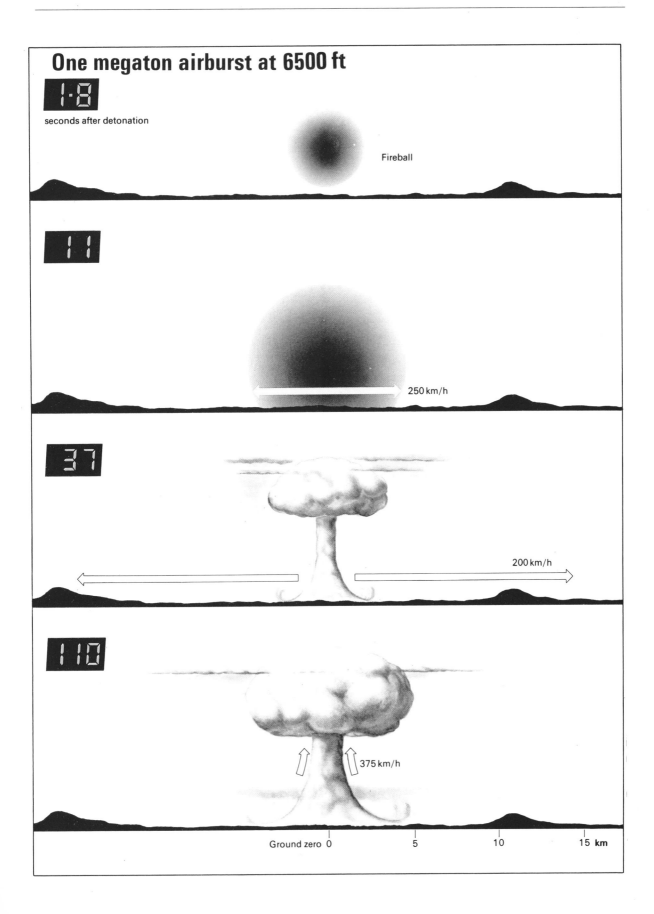

One megaton airburst at 6500 ft

1·8 seconds after detonation

Fireball

11

250 km/h

37

200 km/h

110

375 km/h

Ground zero 0   5   10   15 **km**

Counterforce and Decapitation

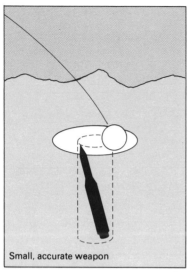

Small, accurate weapon

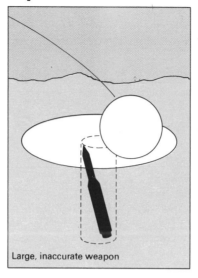

Large, inaccurate weapon

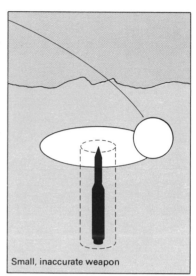

Small, inaccurate weapon

The strategic idea of 'counterforce' means attacking the weapons of your opponent rather than his cities or industries. While this may seem more compassionate, it undermines the structure of nuclear deterrence by inviting strategies and deploying weapons which make fighting a nuclear war seem more possible. Both the Soviet Union and the United States developed and deployed counterforce weapons through the 1970s and early 1980s, notably the SS-18 ICBM and Pershing II IRBM which, because of their great accuracy and destructive power plus speed of delivery, put a much shorter fuse on forces structured, in theory at least, for 'deterrence'. If they are not fired if an attack is electronically predicted, they will be destroyed.

Land-based ICBMs are often talked of as the most destabilizing of nuclear delivery systems because they are fixed targets in the enemy homeland and because they can carry large payloads and deliver multiple warheads with great accuracy, in contrast to smaller and less accurate submarine-launched missiles.

A small but accurate warhead (1) will knock out a hardened ICBM silo as will a less accurate but larger one (2). A small and inaccurate warhead (3), such as current-generation SLBMs, will not, but new weapons such as the US Trident II SLBM are being engineered specifically to have a 'second-strike counterforce capability'.

'Decapitation' applies the same idea but, instead of the weapons themselves being the target, the command and control structures that will give the orders to retaliate are threatened. This is why Strategic Air Command, and now their Soviet equivalents, employ flying launch control centres, while the National Command Authority has a flying command post in the Boeing E-4B 'Kneecap'. An effective counterforce attack will destroy land-based C^3 structures and most ICBMs, while only submarines and alert bombers would be able to retaliate. An ineffective attack would leave most ICBMs able to fire and fail to knock out C^3 networks.

While putting C^3 into the air as means of removing at least some military commanders from counterforce reach, the huge task of hollowing out the granite of Cheyenne Mountain and installing NORAD's computers and command systems was hastened. Meantime, construction of another hardened command post, the Alternate Military Command Center, was begun in a mountain 70 mi. east of Washington. The first National Military Command Center was set up in the Pentagon in 1959 and remains operational, although it is a 'soft' target. Strategic Air Command HQ at Offutt AFB, Nebraska, is another soft target, survival capacity being conferred upon the airborne command centres.

In 1972 work began on converting the much larger Boeing 747 airframe to a flying national command post. The first E-4A NEACP (National Emergency Airborne Command Post), unofficially known as 'Kneecap', flew in 1975. The official

codename for the aircraft is 'Nightwatch'. It is kept in readiness for the President at Andrews AFB, 20 mi. outside Washington and, with the aid of inflight refuelling, can remain aloft for 96 hours, restricted only by the critical running time of its powerplants' lubrication system.

Inside the presidential E-4B there are six compartments—the NCA suite, conference room, briefing room, battlestaff work area, communications control centre and rest area. The aircraft is hardened to resist the effects of thermal flash and electromagnetic pulse (see below). Communications equipment includes a super-high-frequency antenna in a dorsal bulge designed to keep it aligned with communications satellites. A five-mile-long trailing antenna can communicate directly with some submarines on extremely low frequency.

Command centres under rock or in the air are to protect the military order-givers and the civil

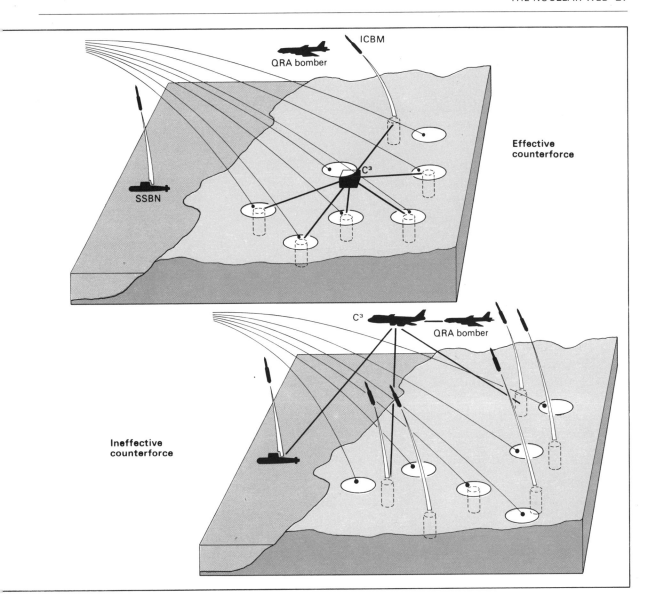

decision-takers. Whether the President could reach Nightwatch or an alternative command centre is debatable.

The first missile to reach its target would be submarine-launched and could strike within 12 minutes of breaking surface off the east coast of the United States. When President Carter tested the system in 1977, the Secret Service almost shot down the Marine Corps helicopter coming in to snatch the supreme commander off the White House lawn. Operation Ivy League, a war game plan played out in 1982, saw the White House being vaporized in the opening moves, with the President inside it.

However, whether the President survives and whether or not the command centres ride out an attack, their communications must still be able to function. After the 1961 Cuba missile crisis, the jealously guarded independent communications and command systems of the US services were slowly brought under the new National Military Command System. President Kennedy discovered during the crisis that, while parts of the US strategic forces were under his executive control, others were not. The US Navy, for example, conducted aggressive anti-submarine warfare in the Atlantic throughout the crisis with no sanction from the presidential commander-in-chief.

It seemed at the time that new communications and computer technology really could put the sprawling war machine under tight executive control. The beginnings of the resulting World Wide Military Command and Control System (WWMCCS or 'Wimex') were sketched in, its development being greatly accelerated in the late 1960s and early 1970s. The E-4A programme was launched, the EC-135 programme was expanded and much more emphasis placed on satellite communication. The essence of the Wimex was 26 computerized communication nodes,

which would link the US armed forces at every level of command with an integrated communications and data resource system. There have been problems—the computers initially used were mismatched to the task and political bickering was the result. The false alerts at NORAD in 1980-81, when simulation tapes loaded in the computer showed up as the real thing, led to more intense political scrutiny. When SPADOC, the Space Operations Center, was moved into Cheyenne Mountain, the military were authorized to specify their own computers. This was because the new mission could not be handled by the existing system, which had become operational far later than originally planned and was by then already lagging behind non-military developments in computer technology. IBM, the company which had lost the original contract to Honeywell, created a separate system within the Wimex for the most critical element of the mission—command and control of the forces which would execute the grand US strategic plan, the SIOP (Single Integrated Operational Plan).

This system is called the MEECN (the Minimum Essential Emergency Communications Network), and includes the National Military Command Center and its alternate, plus the Airborne Command Post. It is subject to constant update and improvement to ensure the survival of communication with the missiles, submarines and aircraft of the SIOP forces.

The big unified commands of the US armed forces—Atlantic Command, European Command, Pacific Command, Readiness Command, Southern Command and the Rapid Deployment Joint Task Force (now called Central Command)—have responsibility for Wimex operations in their spheres of authority, while Aerospace Defense Command, SAC and Military Airlift Command oversee their special interests within it.

SAC's key elements are: the Primary Alerting System, a voice system for passing alert and launch orders; Giant Talk, a high-frequency radio net based on 14 worldwide ground stations and used for positive control of aircraft in the air; Green Pine, a VHF radio network for aircraft flying in the Arctic; a low-frequency communication system (SLFCS) with

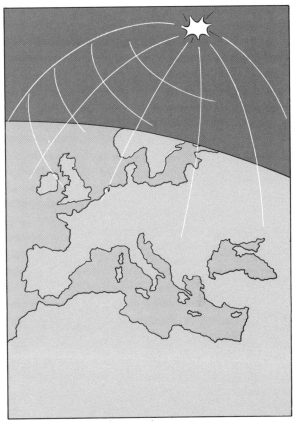

Above: The EMP propagation pattern of a one-megaton burst outside the atmosphere.
Left: Inside the Combat Operations Centre of North American Aerospace Defense Command. Information from early-warning satellites and radar networks is processed by computer to show up simultaneously on the big board.

survival capacity; and a Post Attack Command Control System (PACCS), an alternate C^3 headquarters to Offutt.

Electromagnetic pulse (EMP)

The greatest threat to C^3 networks is the so-called 'electromagnetic pulse' associated with nuclear detonations—a burst of intense radiation covering the frequency spectrum up to several hundred megahertz and inducing very high currents and voltages in cabling and metal structures. Power lines, telephone cables, TV and radio, computers—in fact anything connected to a power line or antenna, would burn out and impart a severe shock to anyone in contact with the collector. An airburst high in the atmosphere would induce EMP effects over a very wide area; indeed three IMT airbursts could cover the continental United States. The efforts to 'harden' C^3 systems are looked at in detail later on.

C^3

Massive investment is being made in C^3 programmes which enable military commanders to retain control of their forces and to make instant assessments of the 'progress' of a nuclear attack, inbound or offensive. But the problems of getting political leaders into places of safety where they would be able to communicate with one another seem insoluble. As political and military leaders become legitimate targets, with ballistic missiles being used as gigantic assassins' bullets, the chances of 'feasible escalation control' or 'war termination' became more remote. How would the President of the United States, for example, communicate with the West German Chancellor on a decision to launch a Pershing II missile that might strike a control bunker outside Moscow within six minutes? How easily could the President reach any Soviet leader to agree to hold back before the full and final military plans were locked in? The hot-line telex machine between Washington and Moscow sits above ground in the Pentagon, relying on 1950s technology, and would be blown away in the opening stages of direct nuclear exchange between the superpowers.

2
The
Making
of
Nuclear
Strategy

After the first atomic test and the dropping of the bombs on Hiroshima and Nagasaki there were no nuclear weapons in the world—they had all been detonated. Of course, the fissile material and the technology were there to build more—and still more. Spurred on by the existence of a Soviet bomb, by 1955 the United States had amassed a stockpile of 2000 weapons. The nuclear world order of today, however, only really began with the Soviet ability to match the United States, not just in destructive power but also in the ability to carry it to the heartland of the enemy—a process which was completed in the 1970s. The US inventory peaked in 1967 at a total of 32,000 individually triggered weapons. Today the numbers have fallen to 25,000, but there are plans to increase them again. The Soviet Union has striven to catch up in numbers of launchers but still lags in numbers of warheads. What possible thought process lies behind the *military* imperatives for more and more destructive nuclear power?

A major reason for the strategy of security through nuclear head-counting is in the physics of the weapons themselves. Once manufactured, fissionable material stays with you. A nuclear device cannot be defused and made safe like a conventional bomb or towed to a breaker's yard. The pressures within the military system to apply or recycle this material from obsolete weapons and make it suitable for new requirements are strong. Thus, in the 1950s military and naval leaders clamoured for specialized nuclear weapons. Nuclear artillery was developed; then nuclear weapons for use at sea, such as anti-aircraft or anti-submarine devices. Then came mines, land-based air defence, air-to-air missiles and so on, while the fissile material production base was expanded to meet their needs. More and more requirements were generated and the availability of new weapons and delivery capabilities strongly influenced doctrinal decisions, not the other way round. Thus, new hardware often opens up possibilities beyond the policy that sought their acquisition. Because modern technology has the capacity to deliver new offensive or defensive abilities such as 'stealth' bombers or space-based laser defence, it can grant strategic advantages which, rather than increasing security, become incentives to attack before the balance is upset.

The military obsession with balance is another factor. Because the adversary develops a weapon or proves the technology for a certain system, the imperative is to match it, deployment for deployment, technology for technology. The new generation of US strategic weapons, the Peacekeeper ICBM and Trident I SLBM, are very accurate and have crushing counterforce potential, which went well beyond the needs of perceived US strategy when they were first designed, but which ideally suits the strategy that is articulated today. The Soviet Blackjack bomber is a mirror of the American B-1B, both at vast expense, while Soviet air defence at the same time is striving to

Above: The Boeing B-29 Superfortress, the first nuclear weapon delivery system. These long-range bombers were operational exclusively in the Pacific.

prove that the day of the manned, penetrating bomber is drawing to a close.

The age of American ascendancy, 1945-60
For 15 years from 1945 the United States enjoyed a period of unchallengeable nuclear superiority, in spite of the explosion of a Soviet atomic bomb in 1949 and the development of thermonuclear weapons in the 1950s. Without intercontinental missiles and with the long-range jet bomber programme proving a fiasco, the Soviet Union could not get anywhere near its ideological enemy across the Atlantic.

In the Eisenhower era there was little doubt who would 'win' a nuclear war. Along with the rise of Strategic Air Command, with its fleets of forward based B-47s and new, US-based B-52s, tactical and intermediate-range nuclear weapons were developed and liberally strewn round Europe. In the meantime, the huge, expanding US nuclear industrial

Above: V-2 rocket, the unstoppable revenge weapon. The last one fell on London four months before the destruction of Hiroshima and Nagasaki. The combination of long-range missiles and thermonuclear weapons in the late 1950s was the true birth of the nuclear world order of today. **Below:** The desolate, irradiated ruins of Hiroshima after the 15-kiloton airburst.

The colossal Convair B-36 Peacemaker, Strategic Air
Command's first aircraft capable of making a two-way mission
to Europe from US bases. In the late 1940s specially lightened
reconnaissance variants could virtually roam at will at extreme
altitude over the Soviet Union. Experiments were carried out
in the 1950s with hook-on 'parasite' aircraft, making the B-36
a flying aircraft carrier.

infrastructure produced weapons-grade fissile material at a prodigious rate for the ever-expanding arsenal of nuclear systems. These included mines, nuclear artillery shells, Honest John battlefield rockets, Talos shipborne anti-aircraft missiles, Genie air-to-air missiles, Nike-Hercules anti-aircraft missiles, ASROC anti-submarine weapons, free-fall bombs for tactical aircraft, Air Force Mace and Matador cruise missiles based in Okinawa and Germany, Army Jupiter rockets based in Italy and Turkey, Thor missiles in the United Kingdom and nuclear weapons on board surface warships and, later, submarines of the US Navy. By 1960 nuclear weapons were no longer war-terminating city smashers but war-fighting systems, integrated into almost every level and aspect of US global power.

With the continental United States a sanctuary and Soviet conventional power in Europe held in check with minimum expense by the nuclear 'tripwire', a policy of massive retaliation which would 'punish aggression' by attacking Soviet centres of power was arrogant but believable. The Soviet Union, meanwhile, skipped the first generation of delivery systems, developing a few unsuccessful long-range jet bombers, and concentrated massive resources on rocketry. The placing in orbit of Sputnik I in 1957 was a greater blow to American feelings of security than the Soviet thermonuclear bomb had been in 1953. Meanwhile, the Soviet army in Europe was modernizing and mechanizing and the Soviet navy, under the tutelage of Admiral Gorshkov, was beginning to push out from its icebound ports into the wider world.

The huge rocket that put the Sputnik into orbit was relatively crude but it was technically capable of hitting the United States. The development of true operational ICBMs, such as the SS-7 and SS-8, began at the same time, even before the Soviet climb-down over Cuba had so diminished its military pride. It was now clear that one day the happy period of assured US ascendancy would come to an end. With the United States itself vulnerable, massive retaliation in response to a conventional challenge in Europe or Asia was no longer credible.

The policy of massive retaliation had also made US military force less 'useful', in the sense it could not be introduced with impunity into proxy conflicts with the ideological enemy, and spending on conventional forces had been diverted away. The strategic revisionists rehearsed their arguments. Then came the new Kennedy administration, a new Secretary of Defense, Robert S. McNamara, and new policies.

Left: At the height of the Cuba missile crisis in Oct. 1962 President Kennedy confers with US Air Force officers including (foreground) General Curtis LeMay, the near-legendary founding figure of Strategic Air Command. Kennedy resisted pressure for a military solution to the Soviet emplacing of short-range missiles in Cuba and brought off a classic diplomatic solution. **Above:** A B-52 launches a Quail decoy missile, designed to throw off enemy radars. SAC's bombers possessed unparalleled powers in the early 1960s, with 540 B-52s and 1775 medium-range B-47s.
Right: Douglas Skybolt air-launched ballistic missile (ALBM), designed for launch from B-52s and compatible with British V-bombers. Cancellation of this system in 1962 led to a political crisis between the US and Britain.

Above: President Kennedy and Prime Minister Harold Macmillan confer at Nassau in the Bahamas in Dec. 1962. The cancellation of Skybolt left Britain without a delivery system which would keep its V-bomber force credible. The resulting agreement secured the Polaris submarine-launched missile at a bargain price. **Right:** A Quick Reaction Alert scramble at a British bomber base in the 1950s, as a Valiant crew race to their aircraft. **Below:** The second V-bomber, the Handley Page Victor, armed with the Blue Steel stand-off bomb.

The age of Mutual Assured Destruction

The new administration's first budget dramatically accelerated the Polaris and Minuteman programmes already in outline form and boosted spending on strategic air and civil defence. The new Secretary of Defense expressed the doctrine thus: 'We believe in a policy of controlled, flexible response where the military force of the United States would become a finely tuned instrument of national policy, versatile enough to meet with appropriate force the full spectrum of possible threats to our national security from guerrilla subversion to all-out war.'

The doctrine of 'flexible response' was soon expanded to imply that the United States would respond appropriately to any attack and would fight and win at the level at which the attack was made, whenever this might be. This meant investment in conventional forces to revive the utility of force for positive political ends, whether it be the newly raised 'special forces' sent by Kennedy to the jungles of Vietnam or the first nuclear-powered aircraft carrier.

On the strategic level the new policy at first emphasized the doctrine of counterforce. Soviet cities were to be avoided; Soviet weapons were the strategic targets. Emphasis on active air defence and passive civil defence in the United States and the geographical separation of the new ICBM fields from US cities were

part of the same policy. The accuracy and discrimination of manned bombers were used by the USAF to justify the XB-70 Valkyrie Mach 3 bomber programme, and senior commanders began to discuss openly the idea of 'winning' a nuclear war as if it were a normal military operation. But counterforce suddenly seemed deadly dangerous. As the Soviet Union slowly developed the means of delivering a massive blow against the United States, the notion of 'riding out' a first strike before launching an attack on empty silos and deserted bomber bases became less and less credible. The result was a shift back to 'city-busting', holding people, not weapons, as hostages. The doctrine was dressed up in an appropriate acronym— MAD or mutual assured destruction.

The MAD stalemate suited the United States during the 1960s, when its military machine was preoccupied with the war in Vietnam. The technology was ideally interlocked with the doctrine—single large warheads on ICBMs and submarine-launched missiles unable to hit anything other than area targets. The side which targeted enemy cities could be certain of destroying them, while an attacker who attempted to disarm his opponent in a first strike on silos and airfields could not be certain of doing so. The MAD doctrine was expressed in weapon procurement. Strategic forces were sized according to their ability to destroy the Soviet Union in a retaliatory strike. This was blandly equated as requiring 400 one-megaton equivalent warheads which would wipe out a quarter of the Soviet population and half the economic infrastructure. After this, increasing numbers of systems would produce only marginally 'improved' results in mass extermination.

Congress refused funds to re-equip Poseidon and Polaris missiles with the more accurate warheads coming out of the ABRES (Advanced Ballistic Re-entry Systems) programme set up in 1962, and nor were ICBMs made responsive enough to be launched under attack. As a further corollary to the logic of MAD, US cities had their missile defences downgraded, on the presumption that the limiting of damage to oneself was irrelevant, given the assured ability to punish the aggressor.

As superiority turned into strategic parity, the need for arms control became stronger. This was as much to cap the destabilizing new technologies of multiple independently targetable warheads (MIRVs) and anti-ballistic missile defence which might swallow up whole defence budgets as in response to domestic and diplomatic pressures for such measures as the partial test ban treaty. Five disarmament initiatives were concluded between 1963 and 1968, leading to the Helsinki summit meeting and the beginning of the Strategic Arms Limitation Talks (SALT). SALT I, signed by Nixon and Brezhnev in Moscow on May 26, 1972, incorporated a treaty limiting the deployment of antiballistic missiles and an interim agreement on the limitation of strategic offensive weapons, providing for a five-year freeze on ICBM deployment.

The pattern of Soviet weapon procurement and Soviet strategy has not been exclusively a matter of action and reaction. The United States has always led the way in technological development—the first thermonuclear weapons, tactical nuclear weapons, MIRV warheads, solid-fuel, submarine-launched missiles and so on—and every time the Soviet Union has caught up. However, different geography and different perceptions of the source of threats against the homeland have impelled Soviet policy into new directions. The United States faces a single nuclear enemy, with China on the margin. The Soviet Union faces US strategic weapons, US nuclear weapons in Europe, French and British nuclear weapons, with Chinese nuclear weapons to its rear. The solution chosen has been the development of very large liquid-fuelled, land-based missiles located in its heartland to match the long-range threat and intermediate-range mobile missiles to counter the threat from Europe and China. Submarine-launched missiles, ideal weapons of retaliation, represent a far smaller proportion of the total force than the US equivalent.

Initially the Soviet Union's nuclear inferiority forced it to rely on city-targeting, and lack of range again compelled it to concentrate on Europe—for its own sake and because that was where forward-based US weapons were. The first generation ICBMs, the SS-7 and SS-8, were not effective against the new Minuteman force in their silos, but the essential requirements for a new generation, the SS-9 and SS-11, were soon available and, at the same time, the first effective Soviet submarine-launched ballistic missiles went to sea. By the end of the 1960s the original US lead in numbers of land-based missiles had been lost and the gap between the US and the Soviet production of submarine-based tubes was closing. However, Soviet progress was about to be blunted by a new US technical advance, the advent of the multiple independently targetable warhead, which gave each missile launcher the ability to hit a far greater quantity of targets. Once again reaction would follow action and during the 1970s the Soviet ICBM force and IRBM force were substantially modernized in an attempt to close the qualitative gap, and unhardened Soviet silos, clustered together and vulnerable to attack, were rebuilt and resited.

A Blue Steel stand-off bomb on its trailer. The RAF crew's protective clothing is a precaution against the weapon's high-test peroxide fuel. Designed and built by Avro, Blue Steel was an inertially guided, rocket-propelled missile launched at high altitude from a 100-mile stand-off range. Once released, the weapon could fly any desired preprogrammed trajectory at up to Mach 2 speeds, delivering a one-megaton thermonuclear warhead. Blue Steel was in service from 1962 until 1975 on Victors and Vulcans. Longer-range versions and a low-level turbojet-powered version were proposed but not developed.

Chronology

1940

FEBRUARY Peirls and Frisch working at Birmingham University, UK, produce memorandum on a practical military atomic weapon.
AUGUST 'Virus House' German atomic weapon research team established in Berlin.

1942

AUGUST Manhattan Project, US/UK atomic weapon research programme established with massive funding.
3 OCTOBER First successful launch of German Army A-4 rocket (V-2), 190-km range.

1943

JANUARY Central Committee of USSR directs I. V. Kurchakov to organize a new scientific establishment in Moscow to investigate the 'uranium problem'.
– – Theoretical work begins at Manhattan Project, Los Alamos, on 'super' or fusion bomb.

1944

15 JUNE V-1 cruise-missile offensive against London opens.
SEPTEMBER First V-2 ballistic rocket lands on London.

1945

16 JULY *Trinity*—first successful explosion of experimental atomic bomb at Alamogordo, New Mexico.
JULY 509th Composite Bomb Group, USAAF, begins training for atom bomb mission in Utah desert.
27 JULY Potsdam Proclamation. Japan warned of utter devastation of the homeland without unconditional surrender.
6 AUGUST Hiroshima. Most of the population are caught in the open as the sighting of only three aircraft quickly causes air-raid warning to pass. 78,150 dead, 70,000 injured.
9 AUGUST Nagasaki. 40,000 dead, 25,000 injured.
AUGUST US Smyth report on atomic energy for military purposes.
SEPTEMBER Project *Paperclip* brings German rocket scientists and V-2s from Nordhausen to White Sands Proving Grounds, New Mexico.

1946

JANUARY UK Chiefs of Staff report on Britain's atomic bomb requirements.
MARCH First testing of V-2s at White Sands, New Mexico.
21 MARCH US Strategic Air Command (SAC) formed as separate command within USAAF.
MAY *V-VS Dalnaya Aviatsaya* (long-range aviation) constituted by USSR as separate military command. First Soviet ballistic missile unit, formed from two Guards *Katyusha* (bombardment rocket) regiments, to use captured V-2s at Kasputin Yar in central Asia.
17 JUNE Baruch Plan. US delegate at UN Atomic Energy Commission, Bernard Baruch, proposes plan for US to give up stockpile of atomic weapons to an international Atomic Energy Development Authority. USSR refuses inspection of atomic energy projects; Baruch Plan vetoed at UN, December.
JULY Operation *Crossroads*: US conducts atomic bomb tests at Bikini Atoll—air and underwater burst.
DECEMBER General Assembly of UN approves resolution for world disarmament. (UN Disarmament Commission meets fitfully 1947-60.)
– – Spaatz report for USAAF emphasizes importance of retaining foreign bases for atomic strike forces.

1947

MAY Tupolev Tu-4 *Bull* appears at air display, 5000-km range, copy of B-29 strategic bomber.
JUNE First meeting of UK atomic bomb staff.
AUGUST First UK experimental atomic pile at Harwell goes critical.
18 SEPTEMBER US National Security Act creates Department of Defense, United States Air Force, and National Security Council which gives charter to newly established Central Intelligence Agency.
30 OCTOBER Soviets successfully launch V-2 at Kazakhstan.

1948

JANUARY US DoD requests Atomic Energy Commission to produce nuclear reactor for submarine propulsion.
20 FEBRUARY Boeing B-50 operational with SAC.
17 MARCH Brussels Treaty: military assistance treaty between Britain, France, Netherlands, Belgium, Luxembourg, US and Canada.
MARCH Project *Half Moon*: first US war plan to include nuclear attack on Soviet Union in event of attack on western Europe prepared by Joint Chiefs.
26 JUNE B-36 operational with SAC, 16,000-km range.

JUNE First in-flight refuelling experiments conducted by SAC.

– – US Navy conducts experiments with carrier-delivered atomic weapons using P2V Neptune.

JUNE-JULY Berlin blockade.

JULY British Civil Defence Corps reactivated.

DECEMBER French experimental atomic pile, *Zöe*, goes critical.

– – British MoS abandons long-range rocket development.

1949

4 APRIL North Atlantic Treaty Organization (NATO) set up.

MAY Decision to build a British atomic bomb announced.

19 SEPTEMBER Detection of first Soviet atomic weapon test announced by President Truman.

1950

JANUARY US decision to develop H-bomb announced. Arrest of Harwell spy, Klaus Fuchs.

14 FEBRUARY Sino-Soviet Treaty of Friendship, Alliance and Mutual Assistance.

APRIL Aldermaston inaugurated as UK Atomic Weapons Research Establishment.

– – NSC-68 memorandum, prepared by Paul Nitze for National Security Council, emphasizes seriousness of Soviet nuclear threat, inappropriateness of disarmament and necessity of increasing conventional and nuclear arsenals.

25 JUNE Outbreak of Korean war.

JULY President Truman approves stockpiling of non-nuclear components of nuclear weapons at forward US bases in UK.

SEPTEMBER British rearmament announced. UK Chiefs of Staff ask for US bomb-testing facilities and are turned down.

NOVEMBER UK agreement with S. Africa on uranium supplies.

DECEMBER Wernher von Braun arrives at US Army Redstone Arsenal with orders to develop 500-mile-range guided missile.

1951

16 JANUARY SAC B-36s arrive at RAF Lakenheath.

FEBRUARY US Navy AJ-1 Savages armed with atom bombs operational from carriers in the Mediterranean.

20 MARCH USAF SAC 7th Air Division HQ established at South Ruislip, London.

11 APRIL Vickers Valiant RAF jet bomber prototype flies.

14 JUNE SAC 5th Air Division established in French Morocco.

22 OCTOBER Greece and Turkey join NATO.

1952

20 AUGUST Avro Vulcan prototype flies.

2 OCTOBER Boeing XB-52 prototype flies.

3 OCTOBER Operation *Hurricane*: first British atomic bomb exploded at Monte Bello, Australia.

1 NOVEMBER US explodes H-bomb at Eniwetok.

– – US *Teapot* Committee set up to investigate development of ICBMs with thermonuclear warheads.

– – British Chiefs of Staff prepare global strategy paper.

– – Tactical nuclear weapon research initiated by US Atomic Energy Commission.

1953

JANUARY-FEBRUARY First B-47s operational.

APRIL SHAPE Chief of Staff affirms that NATO defence plan for Europe called for limited use of ground troops and intensive use of atomic weapons. (In 1953–4 7000 tactical nuclear warheads are deployed in Europe.)

4 JUNE B-47s arrive at RAF Fairford. (One B-47 wing is operational in UK until early 1958.)

12 AUGUST USSR successfully tests thermonuclear device or H-bomb.

30 OCTOBER President Eisenhower announces basic security policy involving use of nuclear weapons at all levels (NSC 162/2).

AUGUST-DECEMBER British civil-defence spending peaks: building of regional 'war rooms' commences, and London tunnels are abandoned.

– – CIA opens Moscow station at US Embassy.

1954

22 FEBRUARY First UK civil defence fall-out shelter exercise: 10 kilotons on Birmingham postulated.

30 SEPTEMBER USS *Nautilus* atomic-powered submarine commissioned.

NOVEMBER US and Canada agree to construction of Distant Early Warning (DEW) radar line across Arctic Canada.

– – Honest John unguided battlefield missile operational with US Army in Europe: 40-km range, low-kiloton warhead.

– – Matador US cruise missile operational: equips tactical missile wings forward-based in Germany and Taiwan.

– – China establishes atomic weapons programme.

– – Tupolev Tu-16 *Badger* bomber, 5000-km range, enters service with Soviet air force. Myasischev M-4 *Bison* strategic bomber, 10,000-km range, demonstrated at air display. *PVO-Strany*, Soviet Air Defence, established as a separate command.

1955

12 JANUARY US Massive Retaliation concept announced.

FEBRUARY Vickers Valiant B.1 enters RAF service.

14 MAY Soviet Union, Poland, Czechoslovakia, Hungary, Romania, Bulgaria, DDR and Albania sign Warsaw Pact.

1 JUNE'Royal Observer Corps officially given task in UK of nuclear blast and fall-out reporting.

JUNE First B-52Bs operational with SAC.

15 JUNE US and UK sign bilateral treaty for exchange of information on nuclear defence planning and training.

21 JULY President Eisenhower outlines 'Open Skies' plan for air reconnaissance inspection of strategic military developments.

JULY US development contract issued for XB-70 supersonic strategic bomber.

SEPTEMBER Russell-Einstein Manifesto calling for world scientists to work for peace.

26 NOVEMBER USAF charged with control of all missiles in US inventory with a range over 2000 mi.

– – First launch of ballistic missile from Soviet submarine.

1956

MAY UK Home Office embarks on ROC bunker-building programme and secure communications net.

29 MAY Regulus II US Navy supersonic cruise missile first flight.

JUNE US begins U-2 reconnaissance flights over USSR.

26 JULY SAC missile-development programme announced: Titan and Atlas ICBMs, Thor, Navaho and Snark IRBMs.

27 JULY B-47 crashes at Lakenheath, eastern England. Three nuclear bombs engulfed in flames but do not explode.

LATE 1956 Beginning of UK operational nuclear capability.

– – 'Bomber Gap' hearings in US Senate on supposed Soviet lead in bomber design and deployment.

– – UK drops nerve-gas research and discards chemical-warfare stocks.

– – Israel establishes secret reactor in Negev Desert with French assistance.

– – Lockheed carry out first design studies on Polaris SLBM concept.

– – US Army Nike-Zeus development contracts allocated for nuclear anti-aircraft and anti-missile defence system.

– – Mace, improved Matador cruise missile, operational in West Germany.

1957

– – Tupolev Tu-20 *Bear-A* (14,500-km range) enters service with Soviet Air Force.

– – Twenty-two scientists meet at Pugwash, Nova Scotia, for peace conference.

JANUARY SAC B-47s operational in Spain.

4 APRIL UK Defence White Paper delivered by Duncan Sandys: conventional force levels and commitments cut back; manned-aircraft development curtailed; Avro 730 Mach 2 + bomber cancelled; emphasis on deterrence by threat of nuclear retaliation.

APRIL Emergency Committee for Direct Action against Nuclear War formed in UK.

MAY Avro Vulcan B.1 enters service with RAF.

15 MAY Operation *Grapple*: UK explodes first hydrogen bomb.

3 AUGUST USSR test-launches SS-6 ICBM.

AUGUST US Jupiter missile RV survives re-entry and lands within target area on test.

4 OCTOBER USSR puts Sputnik 1 into earth orbit.

15 OCTOBER Sino-Soviet agreement on 'supply of new technology for national defence'.

30 OCTOBER Bell Rascal US air-launched missile briefly becomes operational.

– – FROG (free rocket over ground) unguided battle-field nuclear missile operational with Soviet Army.

– – SS-3 *Shyster* IRBM operational.

– – USSR deploys diesel submarine able to launch two SS-N-4 *Sark* missiles from surface.

– – Tu-22 *Blinder* first flown, 5600-km range with supersonic dash.

– – Regulus 1 surface-launched cruise missile operational from two US submarines.

1958

1 JANUARY 1st Missile Division, SAC, transfers to Vandenberg AFB with Atlas D ICBM (activated April 1).

JANUARY Campaign for Nuclear Disarmament (CND)

founded in UK.

31 JANUARY Explorer 1, first US satellite, put into orbit.

20 FEBRUARY Thor missiles activated at RAF Lakenheath by SAC.

31 MARCH Soviet unilateral test ban. (Tests of atomic weapons renewed 30 September.)

APRIL Handley Page Victor B.1 enters RAF service.

12 MAY NORAD (North American Air Defense Command) established.

JUNE Development begins in US of Subroc nuclear anti-submarine warfare system.

AUGUST First flight-trials of Avro Blue Steel UK stand-off bomb at Woomera, Australia.

4 AUGUST Anglo-US agreement for 'Co-operation on the Uses of Atomic Energy for Mutual Defence Purposes'.

10 OCTOBER Minuteman ICBM contract awarded to Boeing.

31 OCTOBER US voluntary one-year test ban; USSR follows in December.

– – Chinese reactor operational.

– – SAC perfects airborne alert procedures and begins training for operations at low altitude in response to improvements in Soviet air defence.

– – US 8-inch howitzer with nuclear shell operational in Europe, 10 km range, low kiloton.

1959

1 JANUARY Contract awarded for TSR-2 advanced strike aircraft for RAF.

12 JUNE First British nuclear submarine, HMS *Dreadnought*, laid down; reactor and propulsion machinery are American.

20 JUNE Soviets revoke agreement to supply China with nuclear-weapon technology.

8 JULY France refuses to permit stockpiling of US nuclear weapons unless under French control; 200 USAF tactical nuclear aircraft redeployed to UK and W. Germany.

26 AUGUST US extends agreement on unilateral test ban.

– – US-British-Soviet test-ban talks at Geneva.

9 SEPTEMBER Atlas D ICBMs operational with SAC.

1 DECEMBER Antarctic Treaty: area to be used exclusively for peaceful purposes.

3 DECEMBER Three squadrons of Thor IRBMs operational in UK on 'double-key' system.

DECEMBER Blue Steel Mk 2, supersonic stand-off bomb for RAF programme, cancelled.

30 DECEMBER USS *George Washington*, first operational Polaris submarine, commissioned.

– – *1959-63* F-4 and F-104 nuclear-capable tactical strike aircraft become operational in Europe.

– – Mirage IV French supersonic nuclear bomber, first flight.

– – SS-1 *Scud* Soviet mobile artillery missile, 130-km range, operational.

– – *Henhouse* Soviet ABM radar system operational.

1960

4 JANUARY USS *Halibut* SSN with Regulus 1 cruise missile, 800-km range, operational.

13 FEBRUARY French test atom bomb in Sahara.

15 MARCH First meeting of Ten Nation Disarmament Committee at Geneva.

13 APRIL UK cancels Blue Streak fixed-site IRBM programme. Warhead development continues.

1 MAY 'U-2 incident': US reconnaissance aircraft shot down at extreme altitude by SA-2 missile over Sverdlovsk; Paris summit meeting breaks up.

MAY Soviet Strategic Rocket Troops established as separate command.

JUNE UK announces decision to acquire 100 Skybolt air-launched ballistic missiles from US.

AUGUST Convair B-58 operational with SAC.

OCTOBER Pershing I battlefield tactical missile tested.

OCTOBER UK Labour Party adopts resolution for unilateral nuclear disarmament.

1 NOVEMBER US/UK agreement on nuclear submarine base at Holy Loch.

NOVEMBER 'Missile Gap' hearings begin in US Senate.

11 NOVEMBER 'Committee of 100', activist group for civil disobedience against nuclear warfare formed within CND.

15 NOVEMBER First patrol by US Polaris submarine.

DECEMBER UK becomes United Kingdom Air Defence region under SACEUR, NATO.

6 DECEMBER President de Gaulle announces plans for French nuclear striking force, the *Force de Frappe*.

16 DECEMBER US offers five nuclear submarines to NATO for proposed multilateral force (MLF).

– – *Golf*-class submarines with three SS-N-4 *Sark* SLBMs operational with Soviet Navy.

– – British Army of the Rhine (BAOR) receives Honest John and Corporal SRBMs with US warheads under double-key control.

– – Davy Crockett light jeep-mounted missile projector with 2-km and low-kiloton nuclear warhead operational in Europe; remained in service until 1967. The weapon's blast radius exceeded its range.

– – Deployment begins of 30 Jupiter missiles each in Italy and Turkey under joint US/NATO command.

– – US begins development of SAMOS-MIDAS ICBM-site reconnaissance satellite programme.

1961

24 JANUARY B-52 breaks up in mid-air above North Carolina. Two 24-megaton weapons released.

Neither explodes but five out of six safety devices fail.
FEBRUARY 'Looking Glass' SAC Airborne Command Post becomes operational.
– – First ballistic-missile early-warning system (BMEWS) station operational, Thule, Greenland.
18 MARCH Snark cruise missile operational with SAC (deactivated 25 June 1961).
APRIL USAF B-70 bomber programme cancelled.
15 JULY First Minuteman I ICBM wing operational.
JULY Berlin crisis: Berlin wall erected 12/13 August.
1 SEPTEMBER USSR resumes atmospheric nuclear testing; US follows, ending two and a half years' implied moratorium.
OCTOBER UK Labour Party conference overturns resolution on unilateral disarmament.
9 DECEMBER First Skybolt test with RAF Vulcan B.2.
9 DECEMBER Khrushchev announces Soviet possession of 100 megaton + superbombs.
– – US civil defence spending peaks.
– – British V-bomber force reaches peak of 180 aircraft.
– – First US satellite reconnaissance of Soviet Union.

1962

19 APRIL First Skybolt live launch.
22 OCTOBER Cuba missile crisis.
NOVEMBER Soviet missile sites in Cuba dismantled and bombers withdrawn.
11 DECEMBER Skybolt programme cancelled; US proposes submarine-based Polaris and European multilateral nuclear force as alternative.
– – Buccaneer nuclear-capable strike aircraft enters service with Royal Navy, supplementing nuclear-capable Scimitars.
– – Sergeant, US battlefield guided missile, 125-km range, operational in Europe.
– – SS-7 Soviet ICBM, with 11,000-km range, operational.
– – *Griffon*, first-generation Soviet ABM, briefly deployed around Leningrad.
10-12 DECEMBER Nassau talks and agreement between President Kennedy and Prime Minister Macmillan: Royal Navy to get Polaris instead of Skybolt.
– – Stanley Kubrick's film *Doctor Strangelove* released.

1963

FEBRUARY UK announcement of intended procurement of four SSBNs.
APRIL SAC ICBM alert force overtakes numbers of SAC bomber alert force.
25 JULY Nuclear Test-Ban Treaty signed prohibiting nuclear testing in atmosphere; effective 10 October.

30 AUGUST Inauguration of Moscow-Washington 'hot-line'.
SEPTEMBER Titan II operational with SAC.
17 OCTOBER UN General Assembly passes resolution for the renunciation of nuclear weapons in space.
DECEMBER Thor missiles in UK deactivated.
DECEMBER Dyna-Soar USAF sub-orbital manned space programme cancelled.
DECEMBER UN announces air force space weapons project—'Manned Orbiting Laboratory' (MOL).
– – US conducts first tests with enhanced radiation (ER) weapons or 'neutron bomb'.
– – US Nike-X programme replaces Nike-Zeus ABM programme.
– – Installation of Atomic Demolition Munitions (nuclear mines) begins in Europe and Turkey.
– – SS-8 Soviet ICBM operational, 11,000-km range.

1964

MARCH SAC B-47s withdrawn from UK.
MARCH UK Ministry of Defence established.
APRIL Polaris A-3 SLBM introduced in US Navy, 3000-km range, MRV warhead.
21 JULY Organization of African Unity announces resolution on denuclearization of Africa.
1 OCTOBER United Kingdom Warning and Monitoring Organization becomes separate executive branch within Home Office.
20 OCTOBER China explodes 20-kiloton atomic bomb.
5 NOVEMBER US missile levels frozen at 1054 ICBMs, 656 SLBMs.
21-22 NOVEMBER New UK Labour government committee decides to continue with Polaris programme.
– – US 155-mm howitzer with nuclear shell operational in Europe, 18-km range, low kiloton.

1965

1965-73 Vietnam War.
15 FEBRUARY UK fifth SSBN cancelled.
15 MARCH Lance I tactical nuclear missile test-fired.
6 APRIL TSR-2 cancelled.
– – Atlas E, F and Titan I phased out.
– – SS-1 *Scud-B* Soviet tactical nuclear missile operational, 270-km range.
– – UK V-bombers based briefly in Singapore.

1966

7 JANUARY SR-71 strategic reconnaissance aircraft operational with SAC.
17 JANUARY B-52 breaks up over Palomares, Spain.

Four large H-bombs released. Two recovered intact. Two scatter plutonium over wide area.

9 MARCH France withdraws from NATO.

5 APRIL First Minuteman II squadron activated.

JULY-OCTOBER Extensive French nuclear tests at Muroroa Atoll.

1967

8 JANUARY Soviet Union conducts test of fractional orbital bombardment system.

27 JANUARY Outer Space Treaty bans placing weapons of mass destruction in earth orbit.

14 FEBRUARY Treaty of Tlatelcolo signed in de-nuclearization of Latin America (Argentina and Brazil do not sign).

29 MARCH *Le Redoubtable*, first French SNLE (*Sous-marins Nucléaires Lance Engins*) launched.

17 JUNE China explodes three-megaton H-bomb.

22 JUNE First UK SSBN, HMS *Resolution*, sea trials.

JUNE UK Prime Minister Harold Wilson announces government decision not to procure Poseidon.

– – Aldermaston continues warhead research on Antelope 1, anti-ABM MRV.

SEPTEMBER US announces plans for Sentinel anti-ballistic missile system deployed primarily against China and 'accidental' Soviet ICBM launches.

NOVEMBER SS-9 Soviet ICBM with very large throw-weight becomes operational.

– – Rescue and first aid sections of UK Civil Defence Corps disbanded.

– – BBC refuse showing of *The War Game*, post-nuclear-strike film directed by Peter Watkins.

– – Strat-X study in US recommends development of four advanced strategic systems: hardened and mobile land-based ICBMs, submarines and ship-borne missiles.

1968

JANUARY UK government announces disbanding of Civil Defence Corps, AFS and TAVR III.

30 MARCH Spartan US ABM test-fired.

30 APRIL Strike Command formed within RAF.

1 JULY Treaty on non-proliferation of nuclear weapons.

Nuclear-potential nations that did not sign are France, China, Argentina, Brazil, India, Israel, Pakistan, South Africa, Spain.

16 AUGUST First test-firing of Lockheed Poseidon SLBM and Boeing Minuteman III ICBM with MIRV warheads.

24 AUGUST France explodes two-megaton H-bomb at Muroroa.

31 AUGUST Soviet invasion of Czechoslovakia.

– – CIA estimate first operational Israeli nuclear weapons.

– – UK abandons plans to base SSBN depot ship in Indian Ocean to support patrols targeted against China.

1969

10 JUNE USAF MOL project cancelled.

1 JULY Nuclear strike responsibilities formally transferred from RAF to Royal Navy.

6 AUGUST US Senate votes narrowly for development and deployment of Safeguard ABM system.

8 OCTOBER General Dynamics FB-111A operational.

17 NOVEMBER US-Soviet Strategic Arms Limitation Talks (SALT) begin at Helsinki.

25 NOVEMBER US renounces first use of chemical weapons and all biological weapons.

NOVEMBER Advanced Manned Strategic Aircraft Programme announced by US (B-1).

DECEMBER French Pluton battlefield nuclear missile test-fired.

– – Soviet SS-12 battlefield nuclear missile test-fired.

– – US Project Nemesis (to install ICBMs on the seabed, in wilderness areas and in very deep desert silos) abandoned.

– – Shipment of weapons-grade uranium hijacked from ship; Israel is possible recipient.

1970

JANUARY Large nuclear detonation reported in Gorky submarine yards.

24 MARCH B-1 bomber contract allocated.

25 MAY Announcement by US government of deployment of MIRVs.

JUNE First RN Polaris SSBN refit completed.

20 JULY US intelligence identifies new Soviet bomber —*Backfire*, at Kazan factory.

28 AUGUST Successful test of Safeguard US ABM.

– – CSS-1 MRBM operational in China, 1100-km range, 20 kilotons.

1971

11 FEBRUARY Treaty to denuclearize the seabed.

24 MARCH Minuteman III US ICBM tested operationally, 13,000-km range, Mk 12 warhead with three 170-kiloton RVs.

MARCH First Poseidon C-3 patrol with USS *James Madison*, 4600-km range, ten 40-kiloton RVs.

– – Deployment of 18 silo-emplaced SSBS missiles beings on Plateau d'Albion in central France.

– – 'Cornflake saga': Anglo-French talks on joint SSBN operations are so limited they can only agree on submariners' diet.

1972

FEBRUARY ULMS (Trident SLBM) programme accelerated.

4 MARCH Short-range attack missile (SRAM) operational on SAC B-52Gs/Hs.

26 MAY US-Soviet SALT agreements. At Moscow summit Nixon and Brezhnev signed SALT 1. First is Treaty on Limitation of Anti-ballistic Missiles which allows each nation to establish ABM defences only around national capital and one ICBM site. Second is interim agreement on limitation of strategic offensive weapons providing for a five-year freeze on ICBM deployment at then-existing levels.

27 MAY Development of Safeguard ABM halted.

NOVEMBER Command data buffer installation programme on Minuteman systems begins: allows rapid electronic retargeting, replacing manual insertion of target tapes.

DECEMBER *Linebacker II* B-52 raids on Hanoi and Haiphong.

– – Blue Steel stand-off bomb withdrawn.

– – Studies for SLCM Tomahawk started in US.

– – Joint RN/USN studies on conversion of RN SSBN fleet to Poseidon are inconclusive.

1973

27 JANUARY Vietnam peace treaty signed in Paris.

JULY Extensive French nuclear tests at Muroroa.

– – *Delta-1*-class Soviet SSBN operational: twelve SS-N-8 missiles, 9600-km range, 1-megaton warhead.

OCTOBER Middle East War.

1974

APRIL UK Labour government cabinet committee secretly sanctions *Chevaline* Polaris front-end improvement programme. Estimated cost: £250 million.

MAY Pluton tactical nuclear missiles enter service with French Army.

18 MAY India explodes 15-kiloton nuclear device.

3 JULY Threshold test-ban treaty signed limiting US-Soviet nuclear-weapons tests to maximum 150 kilotons.

JULY USA unilaterally destroys stocks of biological weapons.

14 AUGUST MRCA Tornado prototype first flight.

NOVEMBER President Ford and Secretary Brezhnev agree at Vladivostok on framework for new SALT treaty: joint ceilings of 2400 strategic nuclear delivery vehicles (SNDVs), 1320 MIRVed missiles.

23 DECEMBER B-1A prototype first flight.

– – Tu-22M *Backfire* bomber operational.

– – First deployment of Chinese CSS-3 ICBM, 7000-km range, 2 megatons.

– – First deployment of SS-18 very large Soviet ICBM, successor to SS-9. Mod 1 has very large single RV. Mod 2 has 8/10 MIRVs, 2-megatons each with onboard computer.

1975

MARCH First test of US Mk 500 MaRV.

26 MARCH Convention against Bacteriological and Toxic Weapons comes into force.

1 OCTOBER Safeguard ABM system at N. Dakota Minuteman site declared operational (deactivated next day).

– – Su-19 *Fencer* nuclear-capable tactical strike aircraft becomes operational.

– – USSR begins development of SS-17 ICBM, 10,000-km range, 4/6 MIRV warhead, 200 kilotons.

1976

FEBRUARY UK government announces intention of producing tritium in the UK, hitherto imported from US under 1958 agreement.

5 MARCH First launch of ALCM from B-52 at White Sands missile range.

NOVEMBER President Ford authorizes production orders for enhanced radiation ER (neutron) 8-inch howitzer shells and Lance missile warheads.

– – Hound Dog missile retired from SAC.

– – US reconnaissance satellite reports new mobile Soviet IRBM deployed at Alma Ata (SS-20).

– – *Delta-II* SSBN operational with Soviet Navy, 16 SS-N-8 SLBMs.

1977

MARCH US reveals deployment of Phase III airborne-launch control system (ALCS) for Minuteman force.

30 JUNE B-1 cancelled.

SEPTEMBER First *Chevaline* tests at Cape Canaveral.

OCTOBER NATO Nuclear Planning Group sets up Task Force 10 to report on TNF modernization.

OCTOBER Chancellor Schmidt makes speech at International Institute of Strategic Studies, London,

raising urgency of European nuclear imbalance.
– – *Delta-III* SSBN operational with Soviet Navy: 16 SS-N-18 SLBMs, 9000-km range, 3-kiloton MIRVs.
– – First reports in West of Soviet charged-particle beam weapons.
– – First flight of prototype Stealth aircraft.
– – USSR begins deployment of SS-20 mobile IRBMs in western Russia and Soviet Far East, 3700-km range, three MIRV warheads.
– – Cobra Dane phased array ICBM-detecting radar operational in US Aleutian Islands.

1978

JANUARY Two Polaris replacement committees set up in UK MoD, Foreign and Commonwealth Office.
APRIL President Carter announces decision to postpone production of ER weapons.
MAY Advanced development programme for Pershing II missile finally completed.
MAY-1 JULY United Nations Special Session on Disarmament.
NOVEMBER UK Polaris Replacement Committee reports. Submarine-based system must be sanctioned by the end of 1980.

1979

JANUARY At Guadeloupe summit, Callaghan-Carter talks on Polaris replacement.
FEBRUARY Full development contract awarded to Martin Marietta for Pershing II.
9 APRIL Last Nike-Hercules/Hawk SAM systems protecting US cities deactivated.
MAY New UK Conservative government sets up MISC 7 Cabinet Committee to consider NATO TNF modernization.
JUNE SALT 2 signed in Vienna. Treaty to last until 1985. SNDVs to be limited to 2250, ALCM carriers to 1320, MIRVed IRBMs to 1200, MIRVed ICBMs to 820, heavy MIRVed ICBMs to 308. Question of mobile missiles, ground- and sea-launched cruise missiles and Tu-22M not resolved.
SEPTEMBER US satellite records double flash associated with nuclear weapon test in South Atlantic. South African or Israeli weapon test postulated.
6 OCTOBER USSR announces troop withdrawals from East Germany. Brezhnev offers reductions in SS-20 deployment conditional on non-deployment in Europe of Pershing II and GLCMs.
20 OCTOBER First operational deployment of Trident I SLBM in converted Poseidon SSBN.
1 DECEMBER USAF Aerospace Defense Command (ADCOM) disestablished; space surveillance and missile warning resources absorbed by SAC.
DECEMBER Deployment begins of Mk 12A advanced

RV on Minuteman IIIs.
12 DECEMBER NATO ministers announce decision on modernization of European theatre nuclear weapons —'US ground-launched systems comprising 108 Pershing II launchers' as substitutes for short-range Pershing IAs, and '464 GLCMs'.
26 DECEMBER Soviet invasion of Afghanistan.
– – US suspends military aid to Pakistan in response to continuing atomic-weapons programme.
– – Space Defense Operations Center (SPADOC) established at NORAD.

1980

JANUARY President Carter suspends exports of high technology to USSR, asks for Senate ratification of SALT 2 to be deferred.
JANUARY UK government announces intention of producing enriched uranium for SSBN fuel cores by gas-centrifuge process at UK sites.
JANUARY UK Minister of Defence announces existence of *Chevaline* Polaris front-end improvement programme costing £1000 million.
MARCH UK government releases Civil Defence pamphlet *Protect and Survive*.
28 APRIL European Campaign for Nuclear Disarmament (END) founded.
APRIL US Congress adds $600 million to USAF development funding of strategic weapons launcher (SWL) based on B-1. Wide-bodied ALCM-carrier is deleted.
MAY Flight tests of US ASALM advanced strategic air-launched missiles completed.
MAY First S-3 SSBS (*Sol-Sol Balistique Stratégique*) French IRBM silos operational, 3000-km range, 1·2 megaton warhead, hardened against ABM defences.
29 MAY US Joint Chiefs testifying before Congress claim President Carter's FY 1981 defence budget insufficient to keep pace with Soviet improvements.
MAY China tests CSS-X-4 10,000-km ICBM.
JUNE US begins withdrawal of 1000 old tactical nuclear warheads from Europe.
10 JUNE US House/Senate resolution for abrogation of SALT 1 ABM treaty.
19 JUNE UK government announces plans to deploy 110 US GLCMs at Molesworth, Cambridgeshire, and Greenham Common, Berkshire.
28 JUNE US House Appropriations Committee votes $3·1 million to build binary chemical warfare plant at Pine Bluff, Arkansas.
JULY French President reveals that France has developed and tested neutron weapons.
JULY Pave Paws SLBM-detecting radar sites operational on US east and west coasts.
JULY UK government announces decisions to procure Trident I SLBM from US to arm four new Royal Navy SSBNs.

SEPTEMBER Test-firings of *Chevaline* Polaris SLBM from HMS *Renown* off Florida.

SEPTEMBER Soviet *Typhoon*-class, very large SSBN, launched—30,000 tons displacement, twenty SSN-X-20 8000-km range missiles.

4 SEPTEMBER Iran-Iraq war begins.

19 SEPTEMBER Warhead blown off Titan II ICBM in silo accident. Does not explode.

SEPTEMBER E-4B US AABNCP (Advanced Airborne National Command Post) operational.

NOVEMBER First test launch of French M-4 advanced MSBS SLBM from trials submarine *Le Gymnote*.

1981

20 JANUARY Inauguration of President Reagan. Caspar Weinberger is Secretary of Defense.

MARCH During attempted assassination of President Reagan, secret war code card is lost. It is revealed that Joint Chiefs of Staff hold duplicates.

JUNE US AEC begins the production of tritium intended for Lance neutron warheads.

JUNE USS *Ohio*, first Trident submarine, completes trials, two and a half years behind schedule.

JUNE Israeli aircraft destroy Iraqi nuclear reactor site.

13 JULY Tomahawk SLCM completes first successful submarine-launched strike against land target.

AUGUST US decision to develop and deploy enhanced radiation weapons (neutron bomb) announced.

AUGUST BMD terminal defence validation programme successfully tested at Kwajalein Atoll.

1 SEPTEMBER M. Hernu, French Minister of Defence, confirms new French Socialist government's intention of continuing to develop ER weapons and of completing sixth SNLE (SSBN).

2 OCTOBER President Reagan announces details of US strategic defence programme:

● MX 'race track' scheme to be abandoned; 36 MXs to be based in hardened ex-Titan and Minuteman silos, the first to be operational by 1986. Three alternative basing options to be examined: continuous airborne patrol, BMD protection and superhardening of silos. 100 MXs to be operational by 1990 providing a capacity of 1000 RVs.

● Long-range weapon system (B-1 bomber) under full development.

● 'Stealth' advanced-technology radar-penetrating bomber under full development.

● Continued construction of Trident SSBNs, one per year to be armed with Trident II SLBM; operational in 1989. SLCMs to be deployed from 1984.

● Upgrading of strategic C^3 systems and strategic air defence.

Total cost budgeted at $180,300 million (£98,500 million) over six years—15 per cent of total projected US defence spending.

10 OCTOBER Very large anti-nuclear demonstration in Bonn.

16 OCTOBER President Reagan comments on the possibility of a limited nuclear war in Europe not leading to a full US-USSR nuclear exchange.

24 OCTOBER Simultaneous European anti-nuclear weapons rallies on large scale in London, Paris, Madrid, Oslo, Brussels, Helsinki. UK CND membership passes 300,000.

1 NOVEMBER Exercise *Warmon*, large-scale UK CD exercise.

4 NOVEMBER US Secretary of State, General Alexander Haig, talks of NATO plans to fire a nuclear warning shot in early stages of European war.

5–7 NOVEMBER Public disagreement within US administration on facts of NATO nuclear strategy.

15 NOVEMBER Large anti-NATO demonstrations in Madrid and Athens.

19 NOVEMBER M. Hernu announces French government's forward nuclear defence policy:

New tactical missile, the Hades, under development to replace Pluton; SX IRBM to replace Mirage IV force in 1993; seventh SNLE (SSBN) to be constructed; sixth SNLE to be operational in 1985 armed with 16 M4 SLBMs; five SNLEs in service to be converted to take 16 M4 SLBMs, six 150 KT RVs, 4400-km range.

19 NOVEMBER President Reagan makes 'zero option' offer to cancel deployment of Pershing IIs and GLCMs in Europe in response to Soviet dismantling of SS-20s aimed at Europe.

22–24 NOVEMBER Brezhnev-Schmidt conference in Bonn. USSR offers unilateral reduction of 'certain portion' of IRBM force.

30 NOVEMBER Medium-range-missile-reduction talks begin in closed session at Geneva.

19 DECEMBER Military takeover in Poland. US imposes sanctions on USSR including suspension of high-technology exports.

1982

JANUARY US DoD announces intention of reaching initial operating capability with Minuteman silos for MX by 1986.

– – UK announces re-motoring programme for Polaris missiles and updated guidance systems for submarines.

FEBRUARY US government refuses to agree on date for resumption of Strategic Arms Limitation Talks because of Poland.

– – US government acknowledges intention of expanding production of nuclear warheads. Intention is to scrap 6500 old warheads, and expand arsenal by 10,500 overall to 40,500.

2 MARCH US DoD announces detection by reconnaissance satellite of B-1 type new Soviet bomber.

7 MARCH Test-launch of French M4 SLBM.

11 MARCH UK government announces decision to procure Trident D-5.

16 MARCH President Brezhnev announces moratorium on new Soviet missiles targeted on Western Europe. If US went ahead with deploying new systems, Soviet Union would create an analogous situation for the US.

MARCH US Navy announces plan to dispose of old SSBNs and SSNs by sinking in deep ocean trenches.

22 MARCH Operation *Ivy League*: US wargame involving actual National Command Authorities includes US President's death and full retaliatory exchange.

7 APRIL RAF Vulcan force committed to role in Falklands.

2 MAY HMS *Conqueror* torpedoes and sinks *General Belgrano*, first act of war by a nuclear-powered submarine.

6 JUNE Spain joins NATO.

7 JUNE Second United Nations Special Session on Disarmament opens.

7 JUNE President Reagan affirms intention of seeking dialogue with Soviet Union on strategic weapons. Each side to reduce its long-range arsenal to 5000 warheads, to be followed by discussion on throw-weight and number of land-based launchers.

14 JUNE Pentagon document envisages a 'prolonged nuclear war' if necessary.

14 JUNE Very large anti-nuclear demonstrations in New York.

15 JUNE Very large anti-nuclear weapon demonstration greets President Reagan in Bonn and elsewhere in Europe.

23 JUNE UK Defence Estimates show unbroken commitment to Trident and continued diminution of surface naval forces despite Falklands fighting.

29 JUNE START negotiations open in Geneva.

JUNE First operational RAF Tornado squadron formed.

SEPTEMBER US DoD reports existence of *Blackjack*-A, a new Soviet intercontinental bomber.

OCTOBER UK government announces that RN Trident D-5s will be stocked and maintained at King's Bay, Georgia. Warheads will be stocked at Coulport, Scotland.

OCTOBER New Soviet solid-fuel ICBM fails in test flight.

OCTOBER China launches first SLBM, 1600-km range.

OCTOBER *Chevaline* warhead enters service with RN.

OCTOBER French aircraft carriers *Foch* and *Clemenceau* undergo complete refit to operate Super Etendard strike aircraft and tactical nuclear weapons.

NOVEMBER US government announces choice of Dense Pack basing made for 100 MX ICBMs.

NOVEMBER Yuri Andropov becomes President of USSR.

DECEMBER Boeing ALCM operational on B-52s of 416th Bombardment Wing.

DECEMBER US Congress approves record peacetime defence budget but MX production money withheld.

DECEMBER Last RAF Vulcan in strike role retired.

1983

JANUARY Rockwell awarded production contract for seven B-1B strategic bombers.

JANUARY Japanese government approves transfer of military technology to the US.

JANUARY British and French governments reject Soviet proposals to include their nuclear forces in INF talks.

JANUARY USS *New Jersey* recommissioned, armed with SLCMs.

JANUARY Second group of S-3 ICBMs operational on Plateau d'Albion.

FEBRUARY USAF announces ALCM production to stop at 1500, to be followed by AALCM.

FEBRUARY Warsaw Pact summit proposes non-aggression pact with NATO.

FEBRUARY Dense Pack basing mode for MX rejected by US Congress.

FEBRUARY US Army successfully intercepts Minuteman I with experimental ABM (Homing Overlay) outside atmosphere.

FEBRUARY First test flight of Mirage 2000N, French nuclear-strike aircraft.

MARCH CDU victory in German general election.

MARCH President Reagan announces emphasis on high-technology space-based defence programme against nuclear attack.

APRIL MX basing committee reports 100 missiles to be deployed in Minuteman silos, new mobile single warhead missile to be developed.

MAY US Catholic bishops call for nuclear freeze.

MAY US House of Representatives approves resolution calling on administration to negotiate an immediate and verifiable mutual freeze in nuclear weapons.

9 JUNE UK general election. Conservative government returned with an increased majority.

AUGUST President Reagan announces that warheads not launchers should be unit of account in START.

22 OCTOBER Very large anti-nuclear demonstrations in European capitals.

15 NOVEMBER GLCM components arrive at RAF Greenham Common.

20 NOVEMBER German SPD special conference votes against cruise and Pershing II deployment.

20 NOVEMBER US film, *The Day After*, attracts record TV audience of 100 million.

22 NOVEMBER West German Bundestag votes in favour of cruise and Pershing II deployment.

22 NOVEMBER Pershing II components arrive at US bases in southwest Germany.

23 NOVEMBER Soviet delegation withdraws from Geneva INF talks.

14 DECEMBER START talks break up with no date for resumption.

28 DECEMBER US Army announces initial operational capability (IOC) with Pershing II missiles in W. Germany.

31 DECEMBER UK MoD announces IOC with USAF GLCMs at RAF Greenham Common.

The age of assured anxiety, 1970-83

Multiple warheads, the Soviet emphasis on very large land-based missiles, and the prospect of ballistic missile defence conspired to bury the concept of MAD. The Soviet Union is thought to have begun investigating anti-missile missiles in the late 1940s and the Americans took up the subject seriously in the mid-1950s, with the expanding capabilities of radar and computers as the key to the technology. But it was deduced that an antiballistic missile system could be overcome by saturating it with a large number of small incoming missiles, and the multiple warhead was the answer. The triple-warhead Polaris A-3 became operational with the US Navy in 1964. The first operational test of a true MIRV, with independently targetable warheads, was in 1968 on the Minuteman III and the first submarine launches were made on the Poseidon C-3 in 1970. The introduction

of the MIRV system into the US ICBM and SLBM force increased the number of available warheads from 1054 on land-based intercontinental missiles and 656 on submarines to no less than 7274 warheads.

The Soviet Union, at the same time, with its big liquid-fuelled rockets with high throw-weights, had ideal vehicles for carrying multiple warheads. Test firings of the SS-9 with a MIRV warhead began in 1968 and US intelligence was soon crediting the missile with the operational ability to deliver three five-kiloton warheads, each one larger than any individual ICBM in the US arsenal except the Titan II.

The new MIRV technology, therefore, had already compromised the first-generation antimissile missiles, but it also completely undermined the doctrine of MAD. With MIRV technology, the Soviet Union could, at some point in the 1970s (the Americans could already do it), arm 500 large ICBMs with three

Above: An SS-9 *Scarp* trundles through Red Square in 1967. It was this rocket, a version of which put Sputnik 1 into orbit in 1957, that gave the Soviet Union for the first time a credible means of making massive thermonuclear attacks on the United States.

Right: US ICBM development began in 1953 and the first, the Atlas, became operational with Strategic Air Command in 1960. The follow-on Titan I and II became operational in 1961 and 1963, and the Titan II force peaked at 54 missiles. The GE Mk 6 re-entry vehicle carries an 18-megaton warhead, far larger than any other US missile.

five-megaton warheads and, assuming an 80% reliability, strike their targets and disarm the vital Minuteman arsenal of the United States in a first strike. All the surviving US seaborne or land-based systems could do in return would be to attack Russian cities, inviting the launch of the large number of remaining Soviet missiles against US cities. Under MAD, the side which launched first must lose. Now, the side which lost its own counterforce weapons would be forced to surrender or its cities would be destroyed.

The pressure was strong for the new Republican President, Richard Nixon, and his security adviser, Henry Kissinger, to open a dialogue with an adversary who would soon achieve equivalent power. Three objectives were defined and pursued— withdrawal of US ground forces from SE Asia, normalization of relations with China and the

Left: The Soviet FROG-3, a 40-km range, unguided tactical nuclear missile.
Below: The US Honest John, its NATO equivalent. Short-range rockets and shells with thermonuclear warheads were liberally deployed in Europe from the late 1950s onwards, and large numbers remain despite doubts about how they could be used 'defensively' without destroying West Germany in the process. **Right:** The US Army Lance, a longer-range inertially guided replacement for missiles of the Honest John generation. The 10-kiloton warhead has equivalent destructive power to a Hiroshima bomb.

establishment of a consistent and far-reaching relationship with the Soviet Union Against this background the first session of SALT began in Nov. 1969. The ensuing negotiations included seven formal sessions over the next two and a half years, the so called 'back channel' communications, and top-level talks at critical points.

SALT I, signed in Moscow in May 1972, contained three separate agreements—a treaty limiting the deployment of antiballistic missiles, a statement on the basic principles of mutual relations and, most important, 'Certain measures with respect to the limitation of strategic offensive arms' (interim agreement). This last provided for a freeze, after July 1, 1972, on the construction of fixed-site ICBM launchers, ballistic-missile submarines and launch-tubes. This was further split between light and heavy ICBMs and a trade-in agreement on new missiles and submarines, which effectively favoured the Soviet Union which had parity in numbers, but not in quality, of systems.

It was what SALT left out which was so important. It did not cover strategic aircraft or 'Eurostrategic' nuclear weapons. Qualitative improvements in accuracy and the equipping of missiles with MIRV systems were not covered, nor were land-mobile ICBMs (such as the MX), although the United States made a unilateral statement that it would view

deployment of land-mobile ICBMs as 'inconsistent with the objectives of this agreement'.

SALT I therefore limited only launchers but did not constrain the numbers of warheads or their accuracy. There was reasonable satisfaction that compliance with the treaty could be verified with relative ease, since silos and submarines could be identified by satellite reconnaissance, whereas what went on electronically in the front end of a missile could not.

The agreement was intended by the United States to last at least five years, during which time a more comprehensive treaty (SALT II) would be negotiated. SALT was the centrepiece of the wider foreign policy of detente and it seemed for a while that confrontation would give way to the pursuit of mutual self-interest. However, the Middle East war of 1973, the flexing of energy muscles by the Arab world and the growing Soviet ability to thwart and meet the global projection of American power in the Third World conspired to kick away domestic support for SALT in the United States. The liberals in Congress wanted 'linkage' to the internal liberalization of Soviet domestic policies. The conservatives saw the process as the concession of strategic superiority to the nation's deadly rival.

Limited strategic options

Even as the SALT I treaties were being formulated, US strategic policy was undergoing another revision. In Jan. 1974 Defense Secretary James Schlesinger issued MAD's funeral oration, announcing a new doctrine for the United States, under which 'immediate massive retaliation against Soviet cities was no longer to be the President's only option and possibly not the principal option'. The strategy brought into the equation the idea of war-fighting and the technical means of doing so were going into the triad—the Command Data Buffer System for the Minuteman force which enabled targeting orders to be changed rapidly, the emphasis on command and control systems which could survive, the Mk 12A warhead with a hard-target kill capability, and a shopping list of alternatives within the SIOP. The strategy became known by a variety of names—the Schlesinger doctrine, limited strategic options and counterforce. The ability to fight a 'limited' strategic war at a level of violence which would leave enough surviving assets and individuals to bargain for peace would, it was argued, enhance rather than dilute deterrence.

'Escalation control' and 'damage limitation' became important components for the new SIOP (known as SIOP 5). Some sort of communication with the Soviet leadership during a nuclear conflict was judged possible, while Schlesinger even talked in terms of them being 'reasonable' and 'prudent'.

In fact US defence intellectuals discovered they had Soviet equivalents in the late 1960s—that there were people in the Soviet Union who also thought about nuclear war. In the Soviet Union military men dominated policy making, whereas in the United States, politicians, academics and think-tankers,

changing with each administration, gave the military men a set of plans and a set of tools to carry them out. The discovery of Soviet thought patterns showed how different their concepts of nuclear war were. Deterrence was indistinguishable from defence and war was divided not by types . of weapons employed (conventional, chemical, nuclear, etc.) but by political objectives with 'victory' as the goal.

Schlesinger's doctrine of flexible response demanded more accurate weapons and more warheads for more targets—while simultaneously assuming the Soviet leadership to be reasonable. As the procurement patterns for the new generation of weapons emerging in the 1980s were set, powerful sections of the US political establishment were pointing to the 'new' discovery that the Soviet leaders might not be reasonable but thought in 'war-fighting' terms. Professor Richard Pipes's famous anti-SALT polemic of 1976, 'Why the Soviet Union thinks it can fight and win a Nuclear War', found some heavyweight political patronage. If the Soviets thought about nuclear-war fighting, then so must the US.

Above: A Boeing B-47 of Strategic Air Command, forward-based in Europe and North Africa from 1954 to 1964.

Right: Douglas Thor IRBM, developed by the USAF but emplaced in Britain and operated by RAF Bomber Command from 1959 to 1964. There were 60 missiles under dual-key control, in contrast to the present arrangement for GLCMs.

Jimmy Carter meanwhile won the presidency the same year, convinced that mutual destruction was still as assured as it had been in the 1960s. Himself a former submariner, he declared, for example, that a single Poseidon submarine could inflict enough punishment to keep the deterrent alive, whatever the men with the satellite photographs and decrypts of Soviet missile-test telemetry were saying. Soon he was believing them.

One by one Carter's attempts at arms control collapsed. Unilateral action at home was relatively straightforward, such as truncating B-1 development or halting the production of enhanced radiation weapons, but power politics in the wider world proved much tougher. The Camp David Middle East peace

initiative tailed off into anticlimax. The linkage of human rights with strategic concession was unworkable. Above all, the calm that had fallen over US policy-makers about nuclear parity gave way to alarm as the results in the wider world unfolded. Soviet general-purpose and naval modernization proceeded apace, coupled with opportunist power projection in the Persian Gulf, in the Horn of Africa, in Angola, in the Caribbean and in Central America. Meanwhile, the Soviet ICBM modernization programme was nearing conclusion, complete with MIRVs and hard-target kill capability. The new SS-17s, -18s and -19s, their apparent accuracy and counterforce ability eagerly trumpeted by the intelligence and military establishment, really rattled the Americans, and it was not a rerun of the old bomber and missile gap scares. 'Window of vulnerability,' an expression coined by a Department of Defense official, James Wade, became a fashionable phrase. It meant a period of years in the mid-1980s when the temptation to launch a first strike against suddenly vulnerable US forces would be overwhelming.

By 1980, after the Afghanistan invasion and the disastrous outcome of attempts to free US hostages in Iran, Carter finally abandoned MAD. SALT II, although signed in Vienna in 1979, was stalled in Congress and, following the invasion of Afghanistan, Carter asked the Senate to defer ratification. With the structures of communication and understanding that surrounded SALT now dissipated, in the summer of 1980 Carter signed a new war plan, called Presidential Directive 59, a development, in fact, of Schlesinger's SIOP-5, but which put extra emphasis on command targets and stressed the war-fighting qualities of nuclear weapons and the long-term survival capacity of command and control systems. PD59 further introduced the new idea that US strategic forces should be able to endure a protracted nuclear war, which might last months rather than a few days of 'spasm' exchange, while it also increased numbers and categories of target options to a total of 40,000—far more targets than there were warheads to hit them.

This huge total does not include urban centres. It is made up of four principal groups: Soviet nuclear forces, conventional forces (fixed sites such as airfields, tank depots, etc.), military leadership and communication targets, and economic and industrial targets, which include both war-supporting industries and core economic targets. Target sets from the four groups are allocated as Major Attack Options, Selected Attack Options, Limited Attack Options, and Regional Attack Options, while the plan leaves open options for pre-emptive attack, plus launch on warning and launch under attack. There were also so-called 'withhold targets', including population centres and national command centres which might allow post-nuclear strike diplomacy to continue.

PD59 alarmed many people because here was a US nuclear war plan which seemed to foresee 'winners'

and 'losers'. However, the Carter administration was especially anxious to disabuse the press of the idea that PD-59 was a plan to 'win' a limited nuclear war. It would rather convince the Soviet Union that it could not win by threatening the targets which 'the Soviet leadership values most—its military forces and own ability to maintain control after a war starts'. With the emphasis on finding Soviet leaders in their bunkers, some supporters of the plan went as far as to say that once the KGB and the Kremlin bureaucracy were dead, the Soviet empire would disintegrate.

Ancillary studies showed how 'limited strikes' could be made on government control targets or on core industries such as oil refining. It worked both ways. A 1980 study by the Congressional Office of Technology looked at the effects of an attack by ten SS-18s carrying 80 one-megaton warheads against US oil-refining centres near cities such as Phila-

An early mark of RAF Vulcan taking off. The last Vulcan was retired from the strike role in 1983, after an operational debut in the Falklands the year previously.

delphia and Chicago and along the gulf coast of Texas. More than half the refining capacity would be destroyed, and there be five million American dead. These 'collateral' casualties did not add up to a blueprint for 'limited war'.

In May 1981, addressing West Point cadets on his commitment to higher military spending, President Reagan told them 'I am happy to tell you that the people of America have recovered from what can only be a temporary aberration.' Referring to the demise of SALT II, he said 'Any controversy now would be over which weapons the United States should produce and not whether it should forsake weaponry for treaties and agreements.'

Reagan had trounced Carter in the presidential election with rhetoric such as this but his defeated opponent had left behind in PD-59 a plan and a programme for carrying it out very close to the new administration's promise of nuclear superiority. PD-59's so-called 'countervailing strategy', with its acceptance of war fighting over a protracted period, was eagerly embraced by the new administration, with the additional ingredient that US strategic forces should not only be able to fight a protracted nuclear war—indeed, they should *prevail*.

The Pentagon's defence guidelines for the period 1984-8 afforded the first glimpse of the new thinking. Again the possibility of protracted nuclear war was emphasized (defined by the Department of Defense as anything beyond a single exchange of nuclear weapons). Whereas PD-59 directed attacks be made against specific military and political targets, the new

Ballistic Missile Defence: The Dead End

Research into antiballistic missiles began in the Soviet Union in the late 1940s and in the United States a little later as an extension of anti-aircraft technology. Computers and the capabilities of a new generation of radars made the very fast reaction and data-handling times seem feasible, but multiple warheads came along to compromise the effectiveness of an antiballistic missile (ABM) screen. While the Soviet Union had deployed the *Galosh* ABM round Moscow by 1962, the United States developed the Nike X ABM programme at the same time. However, enormous costs, plus the fact that large nuclear explosions inside the atmosphere would be necessary to knock out MRVs, served to restrain both sides from going further with ABMs. The experimental US Safeguard programme consisted of a long-range Spartan missile **(far right)** and the short-range Sprint, capable of enormous acceleration **(left),** both with warheads in the low-kiloton range. Meanwhile SALT I and the separate 1972 ABM Treaty between the United States and the Soviet Union restricted ABM deployments to two sites each. A Safeguard site became operational for one day in 1975 at Grand Forks AFB, protecting a Minuteman ICBM wing, before Congress closed it down. A relic is the large, phased array radar called PARCS (Perimeter Acquisition Radar Characterisation System), which is still an active component of NORAD's early missile early warning system **(above)**.

strategy put greater emphasis on rendering 'in-effective the total Soviet (and Soviet allied) military and political power structure and inflicting 'very high levels of damage' on Soviet industry. The emphasis on C^3I was even greater (see page 107), while the guidelines noted that the systems had to provide the capability to 'execute ad hoc plans even subsequent to mass repeated attack'.

The war-fighting tools for such a *second strike* counterforce capability, such as MX and Trident II, which are able to evade or ride out a Soviet strike and yet arrive with the crushing accuracy of a set-piece grand assault under a fine-tuned intact C^3 net, are of course about to come on stream in the late 1980s and are the cornerstones of the strategic force moderniza-tion programme.

US defence plans are not made in a political or fiscal vacuum. A month after President Reagan told West Point cadets that SALT II was 'dead', Eugene Rostow, then director of the US Arms Control Agency (subsequently dismissed in Jan. 1983), assured the Senate Foreign Relations Committee that President Reagan had described the strengthening of the US deterrent as 'essential to the possibility of meaningful arms control'. He further confirmed that, in the view of the Reagan administration, SALT II was deeply flawed and should not be ratified and that a new effort should be made to seek both arms control and arms reduction by means of strategic arms reduction talks (START). Pressure from the European NATO allies was also strong, made more so by the modernization decision on intermediate nuclear forces.

After months of bleak unilateral statement and counter-statement from Washington and Moscow, on May 9, 1982, President Reagan announced that the United States would propose a practical phased reduction plan in the START talks with the Soviet Union. According to the President the US goal 'would be to achieve equal ceilings with much lower levels of force', while reducing significantly the most destabilizing systems—in the US view that meant ICBMs. On June 29, 1982, the START talks were opened in Geneva led by Lt Gen. Edward L. Rowny for the United States and Viktor Karpov for the Soviet Union. No other nuclear nations were included.

SALT II was concerned with ceilings whereas the START agenda actually called for cuts. As proposed initially by the United States it would be in two stages. Phase I would reduce ballistic missile warheads by one-third; Phase II would seek to ensure an equal ceiling on ballistic missile throw-weight at 'less than current' US levels. The problem, however, is in the mismatch of the structures of the rival forces. They are not a mirror image of each other.

The United States has more *warheads* (9000) but fewer *launchers* (1944) than the Soviet strategic forces (8400 warheads, 2537 launchers). The US proposal centres on land-based intercontinental ballistic missiles which the administration regards as the most immediate threat to strategic stability. But it is here,

both in numbers and scale, that the Soviet Union has made its greatest investment. As originally advanced, the US proposal would have required the Soviet Union to have no more than 210 large missiles of SS-19 size and upwards (equivalent roughly to MX) and no more than 110 very large missiles on the SS-18 scale. Since the Soviet Union has 308 SS-18s and 360 SS-19s, it would have to reduce its newest missiles by two-thirds to meet the US position of an overall total of 5000 warheads on ballistic missiles each, of which only one half should be on land.

Again, there is a fundamental mismatch—the United States has only 2150 of its 9500 strategic warheads on land, whereas only about 2150 Soviet warheads are based on submarines, with lower operability and greater vulnerability to anti-submarine warfare.

The treatment of bombers presents another area for disagreement. SALT left them largely untouched, whereas the United States has an advantage which will climb exponentially in offensive power with the introduction of air-launched cruise missiles. There have been hints of linkage, cruise missile carriers versus Backfire and strategic air defence, for example,

Throughout the tortuous process of SALT II, the capabilities of the Tupolev Tu-22M Backfire bomber were a major point of controversy. A ban on in-flight refuelling, which would afford intercontinental range, was written into the treaty.

but no more, whereas a prime concern of the Soviet Union is to limit the US cruise missile programme while it acquires an equivalent technology.

Sea-launched cruise missiles are another contentious area. There are large numbers of short-ranged nuclear-tipped cruise missiles on Soviet warships and submarines, geared to tactical warfare on the oceans. They are, however, capable of hitting US coastal cities, but should they be equated with the much longer-range weapons due to proliferate aboard the ships of the US Navy? US Navy SLCMs will have a variety of ranges and warheads, conventional and nuclear, and their radar signatures are impossible to distinguish.

The Soviet counter-proposal was presented in Geneva in Aug. 1982. It was linked to non-deployment of new US missiles in Europe and called for an immediate freeze on new deployments, while proposing a ceiling of 1800 missiles and bombers of all types on each side. With little shift of emphasis during Andropov's assumption of office, a fuller Soviet position was spelt out in *Pravda* at the start of 1983. It called for phased reduction of strategic nuclear delivery vehicles, reduction of all warheads and bombs to an agreed level, no US forward-based systems in Europe capable of striking the Soviet Union, no cruise missiles with ranges greater than 600 km, no heavy bombers or aircraft carriers in agreed zones adjoining each other's territory, prior notification of bomber exercises, and safe zones for submarines in which offensive antisubmarine weapons would be prohibited.

The Soviet proposal, in fact, called for a higher cutback in its own delivery vehicles than did the US one (*see* table), but it did not emphasize cuts in land-based systems. It cut out cruise while demanding that Euro-strategic systems should be brought in. Furthermore, the US proposal allowed MX to be deployed, while rolling back the decade of intense effort to produce the huge Soviet strikepower centred on the land-based ICBMs. Both sides have proposed substantial reductions and both have shown signs of flexibility, but they cannot agree where to start.

3
US
Strategic
Forces

As a result of the 1960s doctrine of mutual assured destruction the United States possesses only offensive strategic nuclear weapons. Its antiaircraft missile defences were dismantled in the 1970s and an antiballistic missile system was built, but activated for only one day. Its earth-spanning electronic early-warning system, examined later, is a means of giving sufficient warning to offensive forces to make the structure of deterrence work. The essence is 'ability to survive'. However destructive the effects of a first strike may be, enough retaliatory weapons must arrive and be able to be launched in time to make that first strike suicidal. That is why in the mid-1950s the so-called 'triad' of US strategic systems began to evolve—land-based intercontinental ballistic missiles, submarine-based ballistic missiles and manned, penetrating bombers.

It was partly a result of inter-service competition, but each had relative advantages and disadvantages in accuracy, ability to survive, range and cost, and from these basics, a set of deterrent strategies could be constructed.

This combination was enough until the mid-1970s when the new technologies available to both sides began to diminish the credibility of the triad. It was apparent that Soviet air defence would be increasingly able to destroy the USAF's B-52 bombers and that the new Soviet ICBMs would be accurate and powerful enough in a counterforce strike to devastate the Minuteman force sitting in its silos. Meanwhile, the United States' own weapon research was proving technology and developing prototypes for new delivery systems and new warheads, which would themselves render the existing triad forces obsolete.

Thus it was that when the Reagan administration took office in 1980 with a commitment to spend a trillion dollars on defence, US strategic forces stood on the brink of replacement and modernization, with new systems available in prototype form. They are the MX mobile land-based ICBM, the Trident I and Trident II SLBM, the B-1B manned bomber, and the cruise missile in its air-, land- and sea-launched variants. In addition, there are improvements to the tanker force and the all-important Command, Control and Communications (C^3) system.

Looking further ahead, research continues on the ATB or 'stealth' bomber, supersonic cruise missiles and space-based antiballistic missile defence. This chapter considers first US strategic forces, offensive and defensive, as they are now, and then the planned programmes for new systems in Chapter Four.

All this, moreover, is taking place against a background of sporadic US-Soviet diplomacy in the Strategic Arms Reduction Talks (START), inter-NATO relations linked to the modernization of US nuclear weapons in Europe and, equally important, US domestic politics, as each step of the modernization plan inches its way through the US Congress, where the pursestrings are ultimately controlled. In April 1983 the bipartisan Presidential Commission on Strategic Forces chaired by Lt General Brent Scowcroft, USAF (Ret), with a brief to review and assess the multiple strands of the strategic force modernization programme against the background of international attempts at arms control, made its report and its recommendations are looked at later. The modernization plan that went in is not the one that will finally emerge.

US strategic forces now

The long-range strategic systems of the United States are operated by the USAF's Strategic Air Command (SAC, universally referred to as 'Sack'), which controls intercontinental ballistic missiles and strategic bombers, and the US Navy, which operates ballistic-missile launching submarines. The US Army has tactical nuclear weapons integrated into its field formations and operates the Pershing 1A intermediate-range ballistic missile in Europe. The USAF controls ground- and air-launched nuclear cruise missiles and the US Navy will operate their sea-launched counterparts. The US Army will operate the Pershing II missile, which is technically capable of striking Soviet soil from forward NATO bases.

Strategic Air Command

SAC maintains nearly 70% of all US delivery vehicles, 1045 ICBMs and 316 land-based bombers. Virtually all the missiles and 30% of the bombers are on constant alert. From its headquarters at Offutt AFB, Omaha, Nebraska, SAC also commands the USAF tanker fleet of 600 KC-135s, now being equipped with new engines, the EC-135 Looking Glass command posts, the E-4A and B National Emergency Airborne command posts, RC-135 electronic intelligence aircraft, and U-2, TR-1 and SR-71 strategic reconnaissance aircraft. A proportion of the reconnaissance and tanker assets and some of the older B-52s are based, rotationally, in the United Kingdom.

SAC's land-based missiles

The total number of US land-based missiles was fixed in 1967: 1000 Minuteman solid-fuelled ICBMs and 54 liquid-fuelled Titan IIs. (Subsequently two Titans have been lost in silo accidents and phaseout began in 1982.)

There are 550 Minuteman IIIs operational, each tipped with a triple-RV warhead, and 450 single-warhead Minuteman IIs. In 1983 50 Minuteman IIs were replaced with Minuteman IIIs, thus increasing the number of warheads by 100.

Some of the Minuteman IIs are committed to 'emergency rocket communications' (ERCS). Once launched they broadcast an alert via Universal Attack Order satellites to other SIOP forces, in particular ballistic missile submarines. ERCS is a last-ditch insurance against the fear of 'decapitation'.

The Minuteman III was the first US system operational with an MIRV warhead. The result of deploying the Minuteman III, along with the Poseidon SLBM, which also has an MIRV warhead,

Strategic bases in the USA

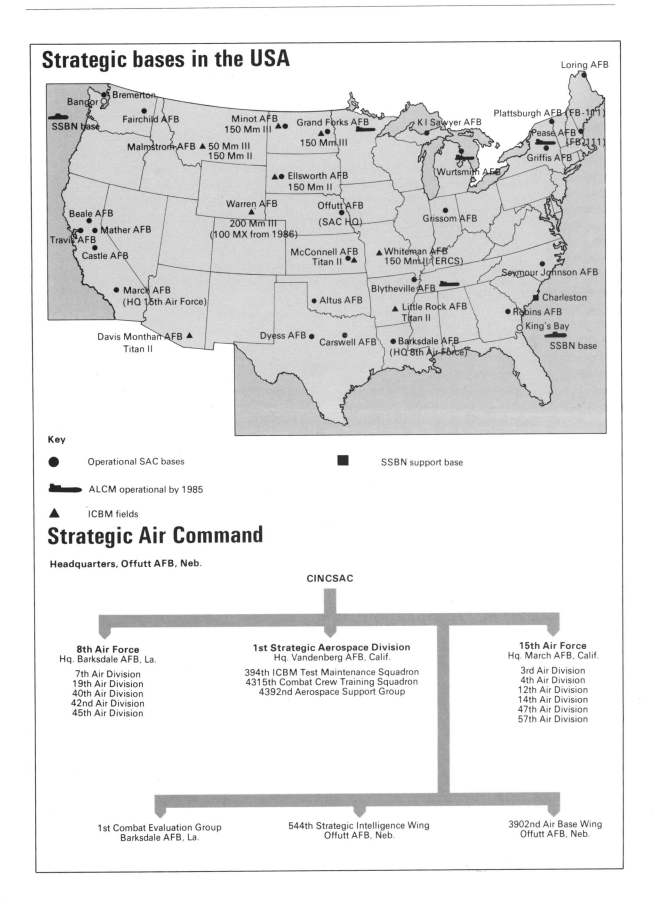

Key

● Operational SAC bases

■ SSBN support base

⬟ ALCM operational by 1985

▲ ICBM fields

Strategic Air Command

Headquarters, Offutt AFB, Neb.

CINCSAC

8th Air Force
Hq. Barksdale AFB, La.

7th Air Division
19th Air Division
40th Air Division
42nd Air Division
45th Air Division

1st Strategic Aerospace Division
Hq. Vandenberg AFB, Calif.

394th ICBM Test Maintenance Squadron
4315th Combat Crew Training Squadron
4392nd Aerospace Support Group

15th Air Force
Hq. March AFB, Calif.

3rd Air Division
4th Air Division
12th Air Division
14th Air Division
47th Air Division
57th Air Division

1st Combat Evaluation Group
Barksdale AFB, La.

544th Strategic Intelligence Wing
Offutt AFB, Neb.

3902nd Air Base Wing
Offutt AFB, Neb.

increased the total number of warheads from 1054 land-based and 656 submarine-based in 1970 to a total of 7274 individual warheads a decade later.

The Minuteman III is a three-stage ICBM with a MIRV warhead of three individual RVs. The first two stages are the same as in Minuteman II but the third stage has improved directional guidance. The Minuteman III has greater range than its silo mate (13,000 km compared with 11,250 km), but is more accurate in spite of flying further. Its circular error probable (the radius of a circle in which half the rounds launched will land) is about 400 m.

The Post-Boost Vehicle is a mini spacecraft equipped with control motors to propel it on its military mission—dispensing warheads in a computer-predicted 'footprint' on ground targets. The normal payload for a Minuteman III is three Mk 12 thermonuclear warheads, along with chaff and decoys (penaids) to confound antiballistic missile defences.

The Minuteman improvement programme centres on both its destructive potential and its own ability to survive. The destructive power of a nuclear weapon is a function of its reliability, accuracy and yield or explosive power. Great efforts are being made to maintain the operational potential of the Minuteman force on each count. Replacement of Mk 12 re-entry vehicles with the new Mk 12A is in progress on 300 Minuteman IIIs and the entire force is scheduled to receive the NS-20 guidance system, incorporating advanced computer techology.

The Mk 12A has been under development by General Electric since 1974. There was a protracted political fight over funding because of the counter-force potential of the system afforded by its yield and high accuracy. Miniaturization of the arming and fusing electronic circuit means that it can carry a W-78 nuclear weapon with a yield increased from the Mk 12's 170 kilotons to 330 kilotons. The length of the Mk 12A is 1813 mm and the base diameter is 543 mm. Because the Mk 12A is approximately 16 kg heavier than the Mk 12 the range and MIRV 'footprint' are slightly reduced. Thus, only 300 out of 550 nose cones will be equipped with the Mk 12A. Completion is scheduled for the mid-1980s, the changeover being effected when missiles fall due for periodic inspection and maintenance.

The ability to survive of the Minuteman force was to be achieved by wide dispersion and silo basing. The force is organized in flights of ten-launch silos, each ten-missile flight having its own launch control centre (LCC). Five such flights make a squadron and

The 100-ton door is open and a Minuteman ICBM is ready for launch. In its nose is the NS-20 guidance computer that can be electronically reprogrammed to take its multiple warheads to different targets within the Single Integrated Operational Plan. The launch sequence begins with 'strategic alert', then passes through 'warhead armed' to 'launch in progress'. After 'missiles away' there is no recall—three 330-kiloton warheads are on their way to the Soviet Union.

three squadrons make a wing. The Minuteman Wings of SAC are deployed as follows:–

Wing	Air Force Base
I	341 Strategic Missile Wing (SMW) Malstrom, Montana 150 M II/50 M III
II	44 SMW, Ellsworth, South Dakota 150 M III
III	91 SMW, Minot, North Dakota 150 M III
IV	351 SMW, Whiteman, Missouri 150 M II
V	90 SMW, F.E. Warren, Wyoming 200 M III
VI	321 SMW, Grand Forks, North Dakota 150 M III

Each wing can be dispersed over a very wide area— the biggest Minuteman field is over 18,000 sq mi.— while individual missiles are placed in silos with a fenced-off surface area of two acres strewn with sensors. The silo is 25 m deep and 4 m in diameter, protected by a six-sided steel and concrete carapace weighing 100 tons. The flight-launch control centre, over 5 km from the silo, is 15 m underground and contains a blast-resistant, shock-mounted capsule occupied by two SAC officers who control a flight of ten missiles. Inside the launch control centre the first warning of an attack would be an oscillating note on the loudspeaker, at which the crew immediately close the blast doors and go on to emergency air. If it is a real attack the speaker will announce, 'Gentlemen, you have received an authorized launch instruction from the National Command Authority,' and simultaneously a printed code of letters and numbers comes through a telex machine. The crew open a strongbox on the wall and check the code inside against the code they have received. If they match, the launch command is valid.

The crew sit in chairs at right-angles to each other, 15 feet apart, and set their individual codes (unknown to each other) to gain access to the firing circuits, then turn keys within two seconds of each other and hold them in place for two seconds. A second crew in another capsule has to go through the same operations, 'voting' simultaneously for the launch command to be effected. These centres can also control a squadron, should other centres be knocked out, and a single centre can override another individual centre's launch command, acting independently of the squadron's. But, once a missile is fired, there is no recall.

From the very start of the Minuteman programme, great emphasis was laid on ensuring the survival of not just the weapons in their silos but also of the command and control system that linked them together and transmitted the orders that would allow the Single Integrated Operational Plan to be put into effect.

In 1962 work on the Minuteman Ground Electronics System (GES) was begun by the Sylvania Systems Group. Called WS-133B, the system has been continually upgraded. Sylvania installed 2000 km of cable and buried radio antennae at each launch

Above: Minuteman III launch from a test silo at the Air Force Missile Test Centre. **Right:** Minuteman silos are hardened up to twelve times atmospheric pressure but have been judged vulnerable to the new generation of Soviet land-based strategic missiles.

facility to provide a double route system of cable and radio, with a third 'redundant' radio backup.

Recent work has been concentrated on 'hardening' the GES and achieving remote rapid targeting. Hardening entails increasing the resistance of the system to shock, vibration, radiation and the phenomenon of electromagnetic pulse (*see* page 23). One answer is to construct cable communications from optical fibres.

Remote targeting is another priority. Target information is stored in the missile's guidance computer as a tape. To re-target the missile the tape has to be changed manually. The missile launch sites are unmanned in their normal alert state, but the missile guidance equipment power is on continuously while the missile's own computer carries out routine readiness checks. The new programme allows re-targeting to be achieved from the launch control facility, which is at least $5\frac{1}{2}$ km from the silo. Much more significantly, re-targeting and launch can be achieved by a flying control centre virtually immune to destruction in a first-strike.

LGM-30F Minuteman II
Similar to earlier Minuteman I but with increased range and payload. Single warhead, operational since 1965.

LGM-30G Minuteman III
Triple MIRV warhead with penaids. First test launch 1968; operational from 1970. Undergoing force modernization programme with Mk 12A warhead and NS-20 guidance system.
PROPULSION: Stage I, Thiokol M55E solid-propellant motor, 210,000-lb thrust. Stage II, Aerojet-General SR19-AJ-1 solid-propellant motor, 60,300-lb thrust. Stage III, LGM-30F Hercules solid-propellant motor,

LGM-30G Thiokol solid-propellant motor, 34,400-lb thrust.
GUIDANCE SYSTEM: Autonetics inertial
WARHEAD: LGM-30F single thermonuclear warhead in Avco Mk 11 RV: LGM-30G 3 × thermonuclear warheads, each 175 kilotons in GE Mk 12 or 340 kilotons in GE Mk 12A RV.
LENGTH: 18·2 m
DIAMETER: 185 cm
PERFORMANCE: Speed at burnout, 15,000 mph +; highest point of trajectory, 700 mi. +; range LGM-30F 6000 mi., LGM-30G 7000 mi.

Work was begun on the scheme in 1966 by Boeing and now, Phase III of the Minuteman Airborne Launch Control System, operational in the mid-1980s, will provide nine EC-135C ALCS aircraft. These will be able to monitor 200 Minuteman, retarget the missiles by remote command and make a vote to launch, even if all land-based launch centres are destroyed. The ALCS EC-135s will be in communication with the Airborne National Command Post (ABNCP), an extensively modified Boeing 747 called the E-4B (*see* page 20), equipped with satellite communications and facilities to enable the National Command Authorities to monitor an attack. Six E-4Bs will be in service by 1987, able to re-target and launch surviving Minuteman missiles, even if an enemy attack has wiped out fixed ground centres.

Strategic bombers

The US Air Force has been in the business of delivering nuclear weapons for almost 40 years, half the lifetime of powered flight. The B-29s that dropped the bombs on Hiroshima and Nagasaki in 1945 were the very first nuclear-weapon delivery systems, followed into service by the piston-engined B-50 and B-36. The first jets, B-47s, were operational from the early 1950s, but were capable of reaching the Soviet Union only from bases in Europe and North Africa. Crews were briefed to make one-way missions—to crash deep in northern Russia and await some sort of aerial rescue. One veteran of this period told the author, 'It would have been better to give us Groucho Marx noses and tell us to joke our way out.'

Then, in Oct. 1952, came the first flight of the XB-52, which, with a range of over 10,000 mi., would spare such embarrassments in the future. It was the prototype for a total of 742 B-52 intercontinental bombers, manufactured in eight major models between 1954 and 1962. The build-up of the complementary KC-135 tanker force began in 1956. By the time of the Cuban missile crisis, SAC's bombers could have inflicted devastating punishment on the Soviet Union without any kind of comparable response.

The commitment to the manned bomber, however, began to tail off in the late 1950s, with the advent of guided missiles with intercontinental range. After a long political wrangle these had come not under Army but under Air Force control. The supersonic Convair B-58 Hustler was operational only in small numbers from 1960 to 1969. According to SAC's commander, General Curtis LeMay, it was too small . . . 'it didn't fit my arse'. The last effort was the huge XB-70 Valkyrie Mach 3 bomber, finally cancelled in 1964. It seemed as if the day of the penetrating bomber was ending fast.

Top left: An FB-111A approaches Pease AFB, New Hampshire.
Left: Standard armament for FB-111As is six SRAMs and/or six B61 free-fall bombs. The FB-111 force of 56 aircraft comes under the control of Strategic Air Command. The far larger force of shorter-range F-111E/Fs is commanded by United States Air Force Europe.

The primary weapon of the existing B-52 fleet before the advent of the air-launched cruise missile was the AGM-69A SRAM (Short-Range Attack Missile), of which some 1140 remain in service with SAC at 16 bases. The B-52G/H can carry up to 20 missiles, 12 on wing pylons **(above)** and eight on an internal rotary launcher, **(left)**. The SRAM is armed with a 300-kiloton W-69 warhead, while some later models have the W-80 warhead of the ALCMs. SRAMs can fly up to 160 km at speeds of Mach 3, with launch at high or low level in a range of preplanned trajectories. The original idea of SRAMs was for the B-52 to blast its way through terminal defences by attacking SAM sites, achieving final penetration to attack primary targets with SRAMs or large free-fall weapons.
Right: Boeing KC-135R testbed aircraft for the re-engined tanker fleet.

Because of the development of the guided surface-to-air missile and highly capable air defence radars, bombers could no longer cruise at extreme height and deliver bombs with impunity. The manned, penetrating bomber, equipped with 'stand-off' missiles to achieve final penetration of the target, would henceforth have to fly low and hug the earth to avoid the radar net. This has been very much the story of the USAF Strategic Air Command's bomber force for the last 20 years.

The B-52 force now numbers some 272, supported by small numbers of training and back-up aircraft. Since entering full USAF service in 1955 the B-52 has undergone numerous improvement programmes and changes of mission. One of the reasons for its longevity is the sheer size of the airframe, able to soak up new equipment and keep flying. From the B-52E model onwards, this massive aircraft, originally designed to cruise serenely in the calm of the stratosphere nine miles high, was modified to operate at low altitude, blasting its way to the target through bad weather, rough terrain and nuclear explosions.

The vulnerable airframes, extensively rebuilt as they are, show the effects of hard usage—their skins dimpled and puckered like a collection of old oil cans stitched together to make an aeroplane.

Two wings of B-52Ds, dating from 1956 and re-furbished 20 years later, soldier on as conventional bombers, but will be phased out by the mid-1980s, leaving the G and H models to continue flying until the year 2000. As a '50-year' aircraft it would be the equivalent of Sopwith Camels fighting in the Vietnam War.

There are currently 16 squadrons of Gs and Hs (two training ones), with 151 B-52Gs and 90 B-52Hs, of which 28 are normally assigned to a conventional role. This includes maritime reconnaissance, mine-laying and acting as a 'Strategic Projection Force' within the Rapid Deployment Joint Task Force (RDJTF). Some 30 B-52s are in active reserve and 223 of all series are in deep storage. Under continuous improvement programmes, the Gs and Hs have received considerable updating of both their offensive and defensive electronic systems, their electro-optical long-range viewing systems (EVS) and satellite communication facilities (AFSATCOM).

The primary weapon of the B-52 force is the Short Range Attack Missile or AGM-69A SRAM, of which there are estimated to be 1140 still in the SAC arsenal. The SRAM was designed to allow the B-52 force to literally blast its way to a target, neutralizing radar and missile sites on the way if necessary. B-52s can carry up to 20 SRAMs externally or on internal rotary launchers. They can fly up to 100 mi. (160 km)

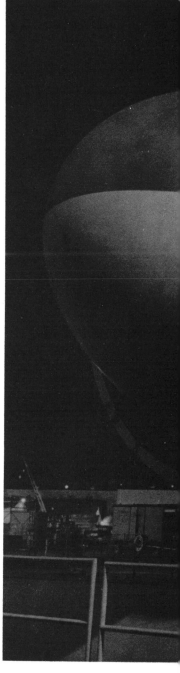

following a ballistic trajectory on inertial guidance or using pre-programmed terrain-following manoeuvres, delivering a nuclear punch equivalent to a Minuteman III warhead at the end.

It was obvious by the mid-1970s that the B-52 force, in spite of its electronic updates and ability to fly low and deliver SRAMs, would eventually be confounded by the ever-tightening net of Soviet strategic missile and interceptor aircraft defence. With the parallel technology of the cruise missile developing, work began on converting a proportion of the venerable bomber force to ALCM carriers. They would no longer be penetrating bombers, but launch platforms for long-range missiles. Full-scale development started in 1978, funding was sought in the budget for the fiscal year 1983 to adapt 64 B-52Gs and Hs to carry the missile, and in Dec. 1982, the first squadron of 14 aircraft became operational at Griffiss AFB, New York. Full operational capability was planned for 1985 when 104 B-52G aircraft would be loaded, each with 12 ALCMs mounted externally. The conversion of 96 B-52Hs, each to carry up to 20 ALCMs, was to begin in 1986.

FB-111A

SAC also currently operates 56 FB-111As, medium-range, high-altitude strategic bomber variants of the F-111 tactical fighter bomber. They can carry up to six SRAMs, six nuclear free-fall bombs or combinations of the two but, in theory at least, cannot reach the Soviet Union from their US bases at Pease AFB,

Above: The last Polaris A-3 SLBM is offloaded from the submarine *Robert E. Lee* in Feb. 1982. Ten of the original Polaris boats were decommissioned from 1981, with eight retained as nuclear-powered attack submarines. The US submarine-based deterrent now rests on 19 boats carrying 16 Poseidon C-3 missiles each, and 12 back-fitted with 16 Trident I C-4 SLBMs. Meanwhile, the first of the huge purpose-built Trident-carrying *Ohio* class submarines seen building **(right)** was deployed to the Pacific in Oct. 1982.

New Hampshire, and Pittsburgh AFB, New York, without refuelling. There have been many proposals to 'stretch' the FB-111, none of which has been put into effect. The nuclear-armed F-111 force based in the United Kingdom comes under the command of US Air Forces Europe (*see* Chapter Six).

The aerial tanker force

The Boeing 707 airliner which ushered in the age of mass civil jet air travel in the 1960s was based on a military aircraft, the KC-135 flight-refuelling tanker, first flown in 1956. Since then 700 or so KC-135s

have been a vital component of US strategic planning and tactical operations worldwide. The ageing KC-135 fleet is being given new engines, initially ex-707 turbofan engines bought on the civil market. It will be subsequently equipped with new CFM56 high-bypass turbofans, keeping its aircraft operational beyond the year 2000.

Ballistic missile submarines
Since its inception in the 1960s, the US Navy's nuclear-powered ballistic missile submarine (SSBN) fleet has provided the 'assured destruction' component of the triad. Sea-launched missiles have a shorter range and are less accurate than their land-based counterparts, suitable for blandly named 'area' targets (which means cities) and not for counterforce 'hard' targets. Once at sea, however, an SSBN acts as a floating silo, supposedly invulnerable in the reaches of the ocean. Nevertheless, like the airborne and land-based missile forces, the US Navy stands on the brink of a huge modernization programme. Indeed, it was the first off the line with the introduction of the

Trident I SLBM (submarine-launched ballistic missile) in 1979.

The number of US Navy SSBNs reached 41 in 1967, each one originally carrying 16 Polaris missiles, but has now dropped to a total of 32. The first of the *Ohio* class Trident boats, armed with 24 Trident I (C-4) missiles, completed trials in 1981 and the next two of ten in 1983. The first operational Trident patrol was made in a converted Poseidon boat, the *USS Francis Scott Key*, in Oct. 1979. There are 31 of the equivalent *Lafayette* class SSBNs in service, 12 now retrofitted with Trident Is to make a total of 192 missiles, and 19 armed with a total of 304 Poseidon missiles. The total number of missiles is therefore 568 SLBMs delivering 5152 MIRV warheads, a sea-based deliverable load of 333 megatons.

Fleet ballistic missile submarine operations
Unlike the USAF and the specified command of SAC, the US Navy's strategic missile force is not under one single designated command, but comes under the operational control of Atlantic Command (LANTCOM), European Command (EUCOM) and Pacific Command (PACOM), answerable through the Joint Chiefs of Staff to the National Command Authority who alone can authorize a launch. Four hundred Poseidon warheads are allotted to NATO's Supreme Allied Command Europe (SACEUR) to cover targets in eastern Europe and the western Soviet Union outside the full US SIOP.

A launch order would arrive as a coded Emergency Action Message. Only by mating it with its counterpart in the submarine's special safe would the captain begin a firing sequence.

In June 1981 Admiral Powell Carter, communications director of US strategic and theatre nuclear warfare, revealed that there is no 'voting' system for launches in the US ballistic missile submarine fleet as there is for bomber and missile crews, who need correlations from outside sources to remove interlocks. In certain circumstances a submarine commander could arm and fire his weapons without coded instructions, even though such a launch would need the co-operation of most of the crew.

Like the first-generation jet bombers, the first Polaris SSBNs to get within range of their targets needed forward bases at Rota in Spain, Guam in the Pacific, and Holy Loch in Scotland to mount their patrols. These submarines average 60 days on patrol and 30 days in port, with transit time to launch areas of between two and ten days, depending on the base location. But, in fact, there is little difference in time on station between a Poseidon patrol mounted from Kings Bay, Georgia, the US Atlantic SSBN fleet base, or from Holy Loch. The advent of the Trident I will cause further changes. The Rota base was closed in 1980 and its squadron withdrawn for refitting with the new missile. Holy Loch in Scotland could easily go the same way, according to recent reports, and a new base for *Ohio*-class operations is under construction at

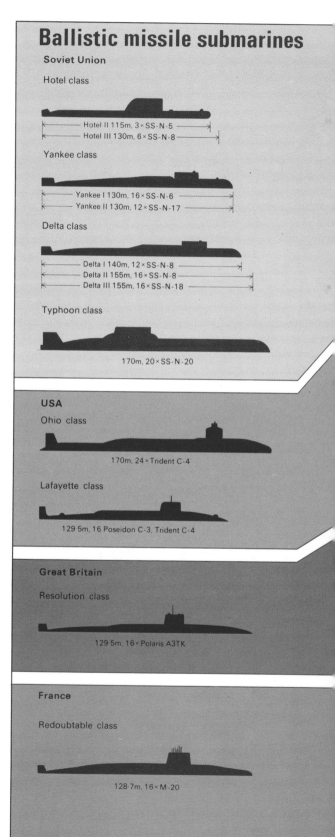

Ballistic missile submarines

Soviet Union

Hotel class

Hotel II 115m, 3 × SS-N-5
Hotel III 130m, 6 × SS-N-8

Yankee class

Yankee I 130m, 16 × SS-N-6
Yankee II 130m, 12 × SS-N-17

Delta class

Delta I 140m, 12 × SS-N-8
Delta II 155m, 16 × SS-N-8
Delta III 155m, 16 × SS-N-18

Typhoon class

170m, 20 × SS-N-20

USA

Ohio class

170m, 24 × Trident C-4

Lafayette class

129·5m, 16 Poseidon C-3, Trident C-4

Great Britain

Resolution class

129·5m, 16 × Polaris A3TK

France

Redoubtable class

128·7m, 16 × M-20

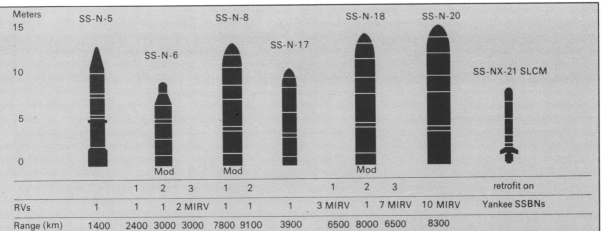

Meters	SS-N-5	SS-N-6			SS-N-8		SS-N-17	SS-N-18			SS-N-20	SS-NX-21 SLCM
		Mod			Mod			Mod				retrofit on
		1	2	3	1	2		1	2	3		Yankee SSBNs
RVs	1	1	1	2 MIRV	1	1	1	3 MIRV	1	7 MIRV	10 MIRV	
Range (km)	1400	2400	3000	3000	7800	9100	3900	6500	8000	6500	8300	

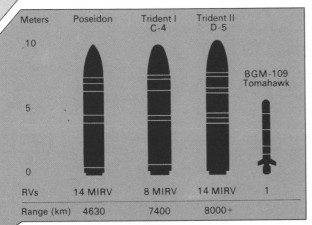

Meters	Poseidon	Trident I C-4	Trident II D-5	BGM-109 Tomahawk
RVs	14 MIRV	8 MIRV	14 MIRV	1
Range (km)	4630	7400	8000+	

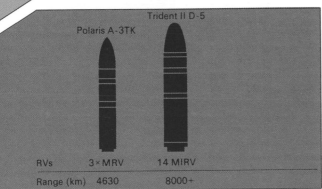

	Polaris A-3TK	Trident II D-5
RVs	3 × MRV	14 MIRV
Range (km)	4630	8000+

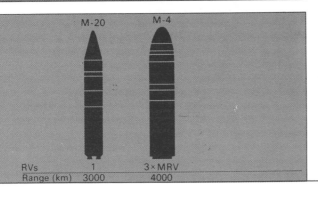

	M-20	M-4
RVs	1	3 × MRV
Range (km)	3000	4000

Poseidon C-3 test round breaks surface. Poseidon was the first SLBM to carry a MIRV warhead.

The missile control panel of a British Polaris submarine. Britain relies on US technology for the missile propulsion, guidance and fire control. The captain and his officers can launch a missile if they have reason to believe that national authorities cannot transmit launch orders to them. The same is technically true of US missile-firing submarines.

Communicating with Submarines

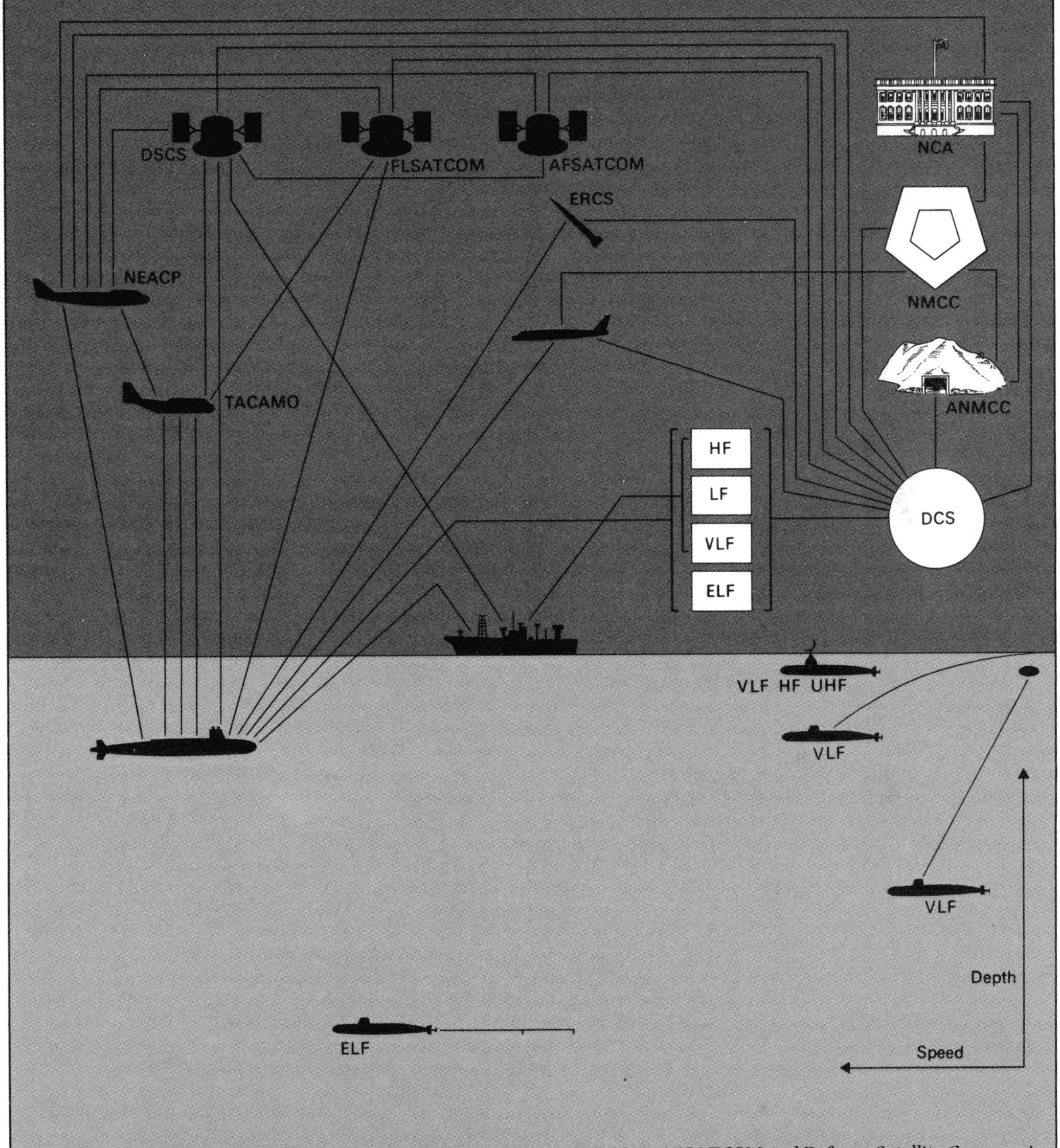

DSCS

FLSATCOM

AFSATCOM

NCA

ERCS

NEACP

NMCC

TACAMO

ANMCC

HF

LF

VLF

ELF

DCS

VLF HF UHF

VLF

VLF

Depth

Speed

ELF

The essence of ballistic missile submarine operations is isolation—SSBNs must run deep, rune alone and come to the surface as infrequently as possible. To function as an effective deterrent, however, they must be able to receive emergency action messages and thus they are as vulnerable to C^3 decapitation as any land-based system. US submarines communicate by means of a variety of systems and on a span of frequencies, all ultimately reaching back to the National Military Command Center and its Alternate via the most secure routes of the Defense Communications System. Messages may be routed by the FLSATCOM, AFSATCOM and Defence Satellite Communications System satellites, via shore stations transmitting on ultra high, high, very low and extremely low frequencies, via TACAMO aircraft trailing long airborne aerials, via surface ships, direct from the Presidential 'Kneecap' aircraft or through the missile-borne Emergency Rocket Communication System (ERCS), which is the last ditch retaliatory launch order system. The diagram also shows radio antenna limitation on submarine speed and depth at various frequencies.

Bangor, on the northwest Pacific coast of the United States.

Strategic-missile submarines are designed to run deep, run alone and come to the surface as infrequently as possible—yet they must be in contact with the National Command Authority and launch missiles from uncharted start points to hit specific targets over distances of thousands of kilometres. An important principle covers both considerations—inertial navigation (INS). This system relies on an onboard reference of time elapsed, distance covered and changes of direction from a known, fixed starting point. A submarine, therefore, functions like an underwater guided missile, with the SINS (submarine inertial navigation system) constantly fixing the ship's location in relation to the start point. When necessary, satellite and radio fixes can update the plan.

Targeting data in a variety of strategic plans is carried aboard each operational submarine. This data, together with a fix from the SINS, is fed electronically through the submarine's fire-control system into the Poseidon or Trident missiles' own inertial guidance system. On launch, therefore, each missile 'knows' where it is and where it is going.

Using a small solid-fuel motor which generates gas and steam in a water boiler, the missile is punched out of its launch tube underwater, boiling and bubbling its way to the surface, where the first-stage motor ignites. As seawater pours into the vacated tube, ballast is provided, steadying the ship to fire the next round. The whole operation takes some 50 seconds.

However self-contained an SSBN's fire control system, it must be covered by the strategic command, control and communication net. The problem is how to communicate with a submerged submarine, for which very large and unusual shore installations are required, and which themselves become an extremely vulnerable target. The US Navy currently relies on satellites and shore transmitters to make emergency contact with submarines trailing antennae some 25 to 30 ft below the surface, to which depth a very low-frequency wavelength can penetrate. There are also now 18 TACAMO (Take Charge and Move Out) EC-130Q aircraft based on C-130 airframes which act as airborne communications centres with survival ability for both high-frequency (HF) and very low-frequency (VLF) transmissions using trailing vertical aerials five miles long. One is constantly aloft over the Atlantic and, from 1983, over the Pacific. In addition, a new aircraft, called E-6, based on the Boeing 707 airframe, is under development and will eventually take over the TACAMO mission.

Using VLF transmissions, radio contact is not constant and may be broken off for several hours. Moreover, because the submarine has to come to periscope depth or deploy a radio buoy close to the surface, speed is limited. However, extremely low frequency (ELF) transmissions are capable of being propagated through seawater to the depths in which SSBNs operate. The US Navy has been experimenting

with ELF for a long time, but previous programmes (called 'Sanguine', 'Seafarer' and 'Shelf') all came to dead ends. Then, as part of the strategic force modernization plan (to be looked at later) proposals for an operational ELF transmitter and for receivers aboard every nuclear-powered submarine were implemented by the administration and approved by Congress.

Poseidon and Trident I
The Poseidon missile or UGM-73A became operational in March 1971, first supplanting, then replacing the Polaris. It had the same range (4000 km), but carried a much bigger payload, with a 10 MIRV front end, and could deliver it more accurately using inertial guidance and onboard digital electronics. Trident I is basically a Poseidon with a third stage. Its longer range (7400 km) vastly increases the area of sea in which the launch submarine can hide. It can carry 8 re-entry vehicles, or 14 over a reduced range.

Range is the imperative behind the development of the Trident I but, although it has nearly double the Poseidon's reach, it has similar accuracy at the target with a CEP of around half a mile (0.8 km).

The Trident's Mk 5 guidance system is similar to the Poseidon's inertial system, but has a sensor able to take a star shot during the post-boost phase of flight, comparing what it sees of the heavens with an onboard computer map.

Strategic aerospace defence
The North American Air Defense Command (NORAD) was formed in 1955 in response to the threat of Soviet bomber attack on the United States and Canada. It remains a two-nation command, but the nature of the threat has changed completely—as has the response to it. Gone are surface-to-air missiles and the directly assigned interceptor fighter squadrons of the US Air Defense Command (ADCOM). NORAD and Space Command, established in 1982 under a joint commander, now control a global network of electronic warning systems stretching far into space, which is designed to give warning of an attack and make the retaliatory forces on which deterrence depends credible.

The warning systems feed into central command and control facilities based at Colorado Springs on the edge of the Rocky Mountains. There NORAD and SPADOC (Space Defense Command and Control System) have a massive battle headquarters carved out of the solid granite of Cheyenne Mountain, where the staff can 'button up' at the first hint of an alert. Space Command has a back-up facility (BUF) at Petersen AFB a few miles east of Colorado Springs.

In peacetime NORAD's sensors and computers are linked to the National Command Center at the Pentagon, SAC headquarters at Omaha and, through that, to the Looking Glass airborne command posts of Strategic Air Command.

US Electronic Early Warning System

The electronic watch on the United States is to give
warning of any incoming attack and make it possible
to launch weapons of retaliation in time—thus making
deterrence credible. Complementary systems watch for
ballistic-missile, submarine-launched, or bomber (plus
cruise missile) attack—all feeding their information
into North American Aerospace Command's (NORAD)
Combat Operations Center under Cheyenne Mountain
in Colorado. The BMEWS (Ballistic Missile Early
Warning System) is based on three sites, in Alaska,
Greenland and Britain, while three satellites and the
Cobra Dane radar at Shemya in the Aleutians also
provide missile early warning.
SLBM warning is provided by two large phased-
array radars, called Pave Paws, watching each
seaboard, while additional coverage of the Caribbean is
supplied by the FPS-85 and shorter-range FSS-7 radars
based in Florida. These will be replaced in the late
1980s by two more Pave Paws radars, based in
Georgia and Texas. The Distant Early Warning (DEW)
and Pine Tree Lines guard against bomber attack from
the north, while two Over-the-Horizon Backscatter
(OTH-B) radars are planned for watching bomber and
cruise missile threats to east and west coasts. More
OTH-Bs are planned for the southwestern approaches,
but they will not work in polar regions.

The early warning system

NORAD's electronic sensors are programmed to deal with attack by ICBMs launched from the heart of the Soviet Union and coming over the North Pole, SLBMs launched from the Atlantic and Pacific, aircraft and cruise missiles approaching from the east, the west and the Caribbean, aircraft approaching from over the North Pole and a FOBS (Fractional Orbital Bombardment System) missile attack that might come 'the wrong way' around the globe. There are also extensive ground-based facilities for tracking military activities in space.

Satellites

Warning begins with satellites watching for activity deep inside the Soviet Union, using radar or infrared sensors which can detect a rocket's exhaust heat. The first warning satellites were the MIDAS system of the 1960s, but these could be fooled by sunlight glinting off clouds. In 1971 they began to be replaced by the orbiting IMEWS (Integrated Missile Early Warning System) and, from 1973, by the geosynchronous Rhyolite system which, because of the height and shaping of its orbit, remains 'stationary' over a fixed point on the earth's equator.

One Rhyolite above the Indian Ocean can spot the booster rockets of a Soviet ICBM within 90 seconds of launch, using infrared telescopes, beaming information to NORAD almost simultaneously via control stations at Guam, and at Nurrangar in Australia. Two further Rhyolites are in geosynchronous orbit over the Atlantic and Central America watching for SLBMs breaking surface. Rhyolites also act as electronic intelligence (Elint) platforms, recording the transmissions of Soviet and Chinese missiles under test.

The satellite system has its shortcomings. The current generation has made mistakes, interpreting events such as fires in gas pipelines or test rockets as actual ICBM launches and they lose track of missiles in mid-course after the boosters burn out but before the warheads and penaids separate. In low orbit they are already compromised by demonstrated Soviet hunter-killer ASAT (antisatellite) techniques.

Ground-based radars

Ground-based systems take over where the satellites leave off. The three huge overlapping arcs of the BMEWS (Ballistic Missile Early Warning System) extend outwards from Clear in Alaska, Thule in Greenland and Fylingdales in the United Kingdom for 3000 mi., covering any missile coming out of the Eurasian land mass towards the United States by way of the Arctic. The Space Detection and Tracking System at Shemya, Alaska, called Cobra Dane, joins in the BMEWS watch.

At Grand Forks, North Dakota, there is a single radar called PARCS (Perimeter Acquisition Radar Characterization System), the sole survivor of the dismantled antiballistic missile system. PARCS backs up BMEWS and can predict the impact points of individual MIRVS, whereas BMEWS can track only the missiles themselves.

Submarine-launched missile warning
Two large, phased array radars called Pave Paws watch the Atlantic and Pacific oceans for submarine-launched missile attack, stretching out in 3000-mi. radius fans from coastal sites at Otis AFB in Massachusetts and Beale AFB in California. Two further stations will be built at Goodfellow AFB, Texas, and Robbins AFB, Georgia, to replace older SLBM warning radars still in service. At Eglin AFB in Florida one of the original six FSS-7 radars survives to watch the Caribbean until the third and fourth Pave Paws sites become operational. Also at Eglin is the FPS-85, an early-model phased array radar which points south, guarding against a Soviet FOBS (Fractional Orbiting Bombardment System) attack. The ability of the Soviet FOBS to attack the United States over the South Pole is believed to be limited to 18 missiles, but the FPS-85 still does not have full coverage of the southern flank of the United States.

Anti-air (aircraft and cruise missile) warning radars
The earliest early-warning radars were built in the 1950s, strung out across Canada and Alaska, guarding against the manned bomber threat, and today the DEW (Distant Early Warning) and Pine Tree lines are still operational, although the equipment is outdated. A programme called Seek Igloo is in hand to upgrade 13 early-warning radars in Alaska.

Radar cannot normally follow the curvature of the earth; it is blind to events over the horizon. However, by using low frequencies and computers to screen out interference, a radar can use a 'backscatter' technique reflecting both the signal and its return off the ionosphere, and, literally, see down. An experimental OTH-B (Over The Horizon Backscatter) station is operating in Maine with two transmitters and five

Above left: A Baker Nunn camera, part of the planned Ground Based Electro-Optical Deep Space Surveillance System, based on five sites around the world responsible for tracking and recording objects and events in space.
Above: A station of the Distant Early Warning (DEW) line, one of 31 spaced out across Arctic Canada, through Iceland to northern Scotland, watching for bomber threats from over the Pole.
Right: Inside NORAD's Missile Warning Centre.

receivers. One is planned for Washington State to watch the Pacific and another in the southern United States is under consideration. OTH-B techniques are affected by the Aurora Borealis, so a radar seeing down into the Soviet Union over the North Pole is not yet practicable.

A new system called JSS (Joint Surveillance System) was inaugurated in 1983, run jointly by the USAF and the US Federal Aviation Authority, replacing the earlier SAGE and BUIC systems which kept radar watch overall on US airspace for military and civil movements. Seven Regional Operations Control Rooms (ROCCs), 4 in the United States, 1 in Alaska and 2 in Canada control 84 radars scattered widely across North America (including some, called Seek Skyhook, in balloons over Florida watching for low-level attack from Cuba). Seven E-3A AWACS aircraft of Tactical Air Command are assigned to NORAD in peacetime with more on order, making random sweeps over the coastal and northern approaches to the United States, with the ability to detect low-flying intruders and direct interceptions.

Space Command

On Sept. 1, 1982, USAF Space Command was established with the telling motto 'Guardians of the High Frontier'. The new command reflected the ever-growing strategic importance of space but its head remained the commander-in-chief of NORAD as well. The vice-commander of SPACECOM is also the commander of Air Force Systems Command Space Division, located at Los Angeles, which controls the Space and Missile Test Organization at Vandenberg AFB, California.

Space Command will group together the following resources. There will be four major bases—at Thule and Sondestrom in Greenland, at Clear, Alaska, and at Peterson AFB, Colorado, which will be the site of the Consolidated Space Operations Center (CSOC). From this centre SPACECOM will control operational spacecraft and will manage all military shuttle flights and anti-satellite units.

Space Command will have responsibility for two operational satellite systems—infrared early warning and the Defense Meteorological Satellite Program, together with their ground components.

Space Command will also have responsibility for the worldwide missile-warning and space-surveillance network. The USAF's Spacetrack ground system traces movements in space from stations at Princlik (Turkey), in New Mexico and California, and at St Margarets (New Brunswick, Canada), Pulmosan (South Korea), San Vito (Italy), Maui (Hawaii) and Mt John (New Zealand). It is supplemented by the GEODSS (Ground-Based Electro-Optical Deep Space Surveillance System) which tracks and catalogues objects in space, using very powerful Baker-Nunn cameras. Five sites are planned with three now operational—at White Sands (New Mexico), Taegu (South Korea) and Maui (Hawaii).

Also feeding into SPADOC is the US Navy's NAVSPASUR line, which tracks satellites crossing an electronic fence strung across the southern United States. There are, in addition, inputs from missile test-range radars at Kuajalein Atoll, Ascension Island, Antigua, Kaena Point, Hawaii, Mt Lincoln Laboratory, Massachusetts, and the RAF radar at Malvern in the United Kingdom.

First Space Wing
This manages the 24 units operating the satellite systems and ground-based sensors.
Space Communications Division
This operates communications systems for space-surveillance and missile-warning systems and data-processing equipment at Cheyenne Mountain.
SPADOC Space Defense Operations Center
This provides intelligence data and operational control by maintaining the status of all defence and civil satellites, and, in addition, operational control of space systems from within Cheyenne Mountain.

Operational units
In 1979-80 the organization of US air defence assets went through a transition. In April 1979 the last missile defences of sites in the US were finally scrapped and the brief of ADCOM (Aerospace Defense Command) was reduced. In 1982 SPACECOM was

Space Command

Headquarters, Peterson AFB, Colo.

1st Space Division
Los Angeles AFS, Calif.
(1st Space Division Commander is also SPACECOM Vice-Commander)

System Integration Office
Peterson AFB, Colo.

Aerospace Defense Center
Peterson AFB, Colo.

Air Defense Operations Center
Cheyenne Mountain Complex

3rd Airborne Command & Control Squadron
Tinker AFB, Okla.

1022nd Support Squadron
North Bay, Ontario, Canada

Surveillance Squadrons
16th Surveillance Squadron
Shemya AFB, Alaska

17th Surveillance Squadron
San Miguel, Philippines

Missile Warning Squadrons
6th Missile Warning Squadron
Otis AFB, Mass.

7th Missile Warning Squadron
Beale AFB, Calif.

13th Missile Warning Squadron
Clear AFB, Alaska

20th Missile Warning Squadron
Eglin AFB, Fla.

Boeing E-3A Sentry Airborne Warning and Control System (AWACS). Tactical Air Command is responsible for maintaining the sovereignty of American airspace, and the entry into service of the E-3A has given it a 'force multiplier' able to detect intruders and direct interceptions from the vantage point of look-down radar, effectively closing the low-level gap. To date there are three AWACS squadrons operating 29 Sentries. The later E-3B has improved over-water radar intercept capability.

established with operational control of the space-based warning systems, and the ADCOM interceptor units were put under the overall Tactical Air Command control.

Air Defense TAC (ADTAC) has its headquarters at Langley AFB, Virginia, and five assigned air divisions maintaining alert at 26 sites around the periphery of the United States, with day-to-day deployments to Iceland and six more alert sites in Alaska. ADTAC currently fields 75 F-106s (scheduled for replacement by F-15 Eagles) and 18 F-15s. An air-defence squadron in Iceland has 21 F-4s (to be replaced by F-15s) and the Air National Guard provides 90 F-4s and 75 F-106s at bases across continental America. Canada contributes 54 CF-101s (soon to be replaced by CF-18 Hornets). Tactical Air Command also has F-4 and F-15 'augmentation forces' assigned to air defence. Three TAC fighter wings based in the United States and equipped with the F-15 will be trained in air defence as a secondary mission.

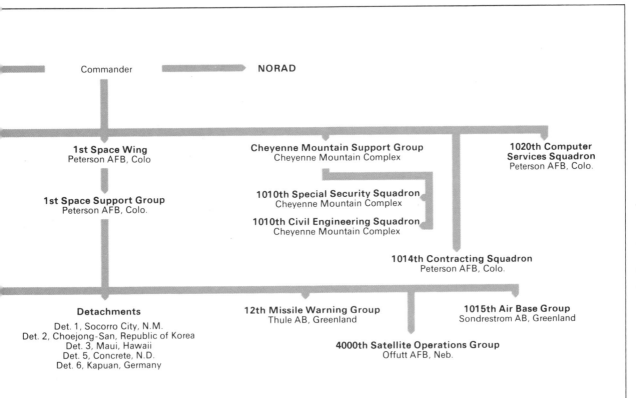

Commander ➤ **NORAD**

1st Space Wing
Peterson AFB, Colo

Cheyenne Mountain Support Group
Cheyenne Mountain Complex

1020th Computer Services Squadron
Peterson AFB, Colo.

1st Space Support Group
Peterson AFB, Colo.

1010th Special Security Squadron
Cheyenne Mountain Complex

1010th Civil Engineering Squadron
Cheyenne Mountain Complex

1014th Contracting Squadron
Peterson AFB, Colo.

Detachments
Det. 1, Socorro City, N.M.
Det. 2, Choejong-San, Republic of Korea
Det. 3, Maui, Hawaii
Det. 5, Concrete, N.D.
Det. 6, Kapuan, Germany

12th Missile Warning Group
Thule AB, Greenland

1015th Air Base Group
Sondrestrom AB, Greenland

4000th Satellite Operations Group
Offutt AFB, Neb.

4
The
Future
Triad

On Jan. 20, 1982, Ronald Reagan took office as President, with Caspar Weinberger as Secretary of Defense, after a campaign in which the supposed strategic infirmity of the United States under Jimmy Carter was a key election issue. By Oct. 1 the administration was ready to unveil a strategic force modernization plan. It was to cost $180,300 million (£98,500 million) over six years, 15% of projected US defence spending. As proposed then the plan called for the following:–

- MX missile to be deployed in fixed silos by 1986, while research on alternative basing modes continued.
- Long-range weapon system (B-1B bomber) under full development.
- Stealth advanced-technology radar-penetrating bomber under development for operation in 1990s.
- Continued construction of Trident SSBNs; one a year to be armed with Trident II SLBMs, operational in 1989. Nuclear-armed SLCMs to be operational from 1984.
- Improvements in strategic C3 systems.
- Upgrading of strategic air defence and accelerated development of ballistic missile defences.

MX Peacekeeper ICBM

The Missile-X, now named 'Peacekeeper', is a four-stage ICBM, weighing over 86 metric tons and capable of lifting 3600 kg (7940 lb) over 11,100 km (6900 mi.). The post-boost vehicle contains the computers, guidance and control equipment and ten independently targetable Mk 12A RVs. The missile's great accuracy, even over a very long range, plus the warhead's capabilities give a CEP, in theory at least, of 250 m and a kill rate against a 1000-psi hardened target of 99·9%.

The MX is more than a bigger, more lethal Minuteman. What is important is the MX's ability to 'survive' an attack itself. To this end it was designed to be mobile while retaining the accuracy and power of a land-based system. The key is the AIRS ('advanced inertial reference sphere') system, which continuously navigates from a true initial start point, allowing the missile to be shuttled about without requiring a fresh computation of launch point.

There were many proposals for using this new system. The one advanced by the Carter government entailed basing the missile in underground closed loops and linear tracks. The provision of 4600 shelters, with 200 missiles shuttling between them, would compel an attacker to target every shelter, in order to be sure of wiping out the MX retaliatory force. Supporters of the MX said the 'shell game' proposal would cost $34 billion. Its opponents said it would cost $100 billion and swallow up nearly half of US cement manufacture over three years.

There have been 39 reviews of MX basing modes in the 15 years to 1983. Some were even more bizarre than the multiple shelter idea, and included dropping

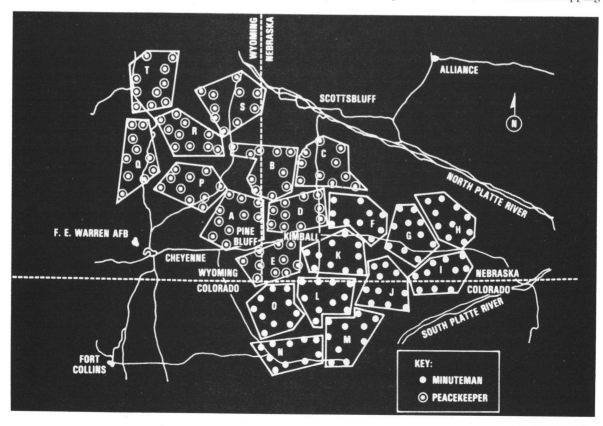

the missiles in the ocean in floating capsules, or mounting them on very large vertical take-off aircraft that could operate from remote airstrips. Other ideas included putting them on surface ships, on shallow-water submarines operating in lakes and coastal waters, mounting them on amphibian flying boats, basing them in giant transport aircraft on continuous patrol, sinking them in deep mines with buried digging equipment for crews to burrow out, digging into the south sides of rock mesas, keeping them on railway stock disguised as ordinary traffic, loading them on trucks roaming the nation's highways, and a 'dash on warning' system in which, during a crisis, a high-speed transporter would move the missile from a central hub to any one of a number of reinforced shelters arranged like the spokes of a wheel.

All were considered—none was adopted, and the multiple-shelter plan was abandoned early on by the Reagan administration after loud environmental protests from the states of Nevada and Utah. As a temporary expedient the Secretary of Defense announced in Oct. 1981 that the first 100 missiles would be placed in existing Minuteman silos, apparently a better idea than putting them into warehouses. Congress did not agree and in March 1982 demanded new solutions before funding further development.

In Nov. 1982, therefore, the administration advanced the so-called 'dense-pack' solution. The missiles would be deployed in a 14-mile-long, north-south column of silos, each 1800 ft apart. This relied on the theory of 'nuclear fratricide'—the idea being that if a Soviet missile attack was launched on 100 MX missiles grouped close together in a super-hardened cluster, the first incoming ICBM to explode would knock out its companions following close behind. As more than one direct hit would be needed to root out the whole force, enough MX missiles would survive to retaliate. The window of vulnerability would be closed and deterrence maintained—or so the argument went.

Critics doubted the technical basis of a theory which could be tested only in an actual war, and even if it worked it would invite a Soviet second strike. The Joint Chiefs of Staff themselves were divided, three to two against the concept of dense pack. The proposal to base the cluster of 'Peacekeepers' at Francis E Warren AFB, Cheyenne, Wyoming, lasted less than a month. Congress remained sceptical, voting research and development funds but no production money, and called on President Reagan to submit a new basing mode recommendation by March 1, 1983.

The Scowcroft Report

Faced with a political impasse, the administration convened a special bipartisan Commission on

Left: 100 Peacekeeper missiles will, on current plans, be based in existing silos at F E Warren AFB, Wyoming. The installation is about 200 km across.

MX basing modes

Dense Pack

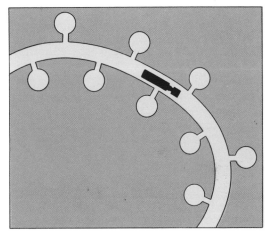

Shell Game

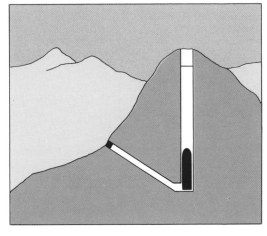

Deep under-mountain basing

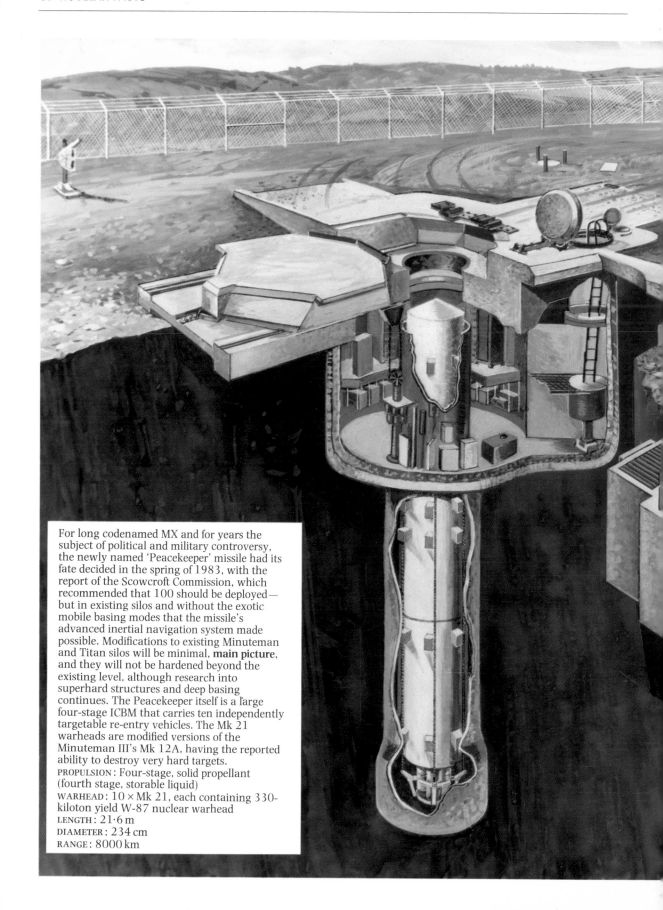

For long codenamed MX and for years the subject of political and military controversy, the newly named 'Peacekeeper' missile had its fate decided in the spring of 1983, with the report of the Scowcroft Commission, which recommended that 100 should be deployed— but in existing silos and without the exotic mobile basing modes that the missile's advanced inertial navigation system made possible. Modifications to existing Minuteman and Titan silos will be minimal, **main picture**, and they will not be hardened beyond the existing level, although research into superhard structures and deep basing continues. The Peacekeeper itself is a large four-stage ICBM that carries ten independently targetable re-entry vehicles. The Mk 21 warheads are modified versions of the Minuteman III's Mk 12A, having the reported ability to destroy very hard targets.

PROPULSION: Four-stage, solid propellant (fourth stage, storable liquid)

WARHEAD: 10 × Mk 21, each containing 330-kiloton yield W-87 nuclear warhead

LENGTH: 21·6 m

DIAMETER: 234 cm

RANGE: 8000 km

Peacekeeper Missile

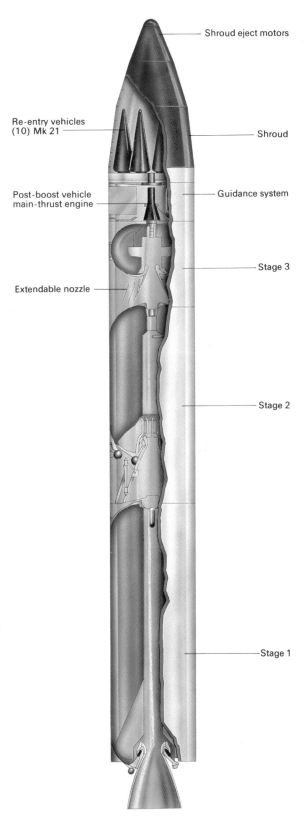

Shroud eject motors

Re-entry vehicles (10) Mk 21

Shroud

Post-boost vehicle main-thrust engine

Guidance system

Stage 3

Extendable nozzle

Stage 2

Stage 1

Strategic Forces, chaired by a retired Air Force general and National Security Council member—Lt General Brent Scowcroft. His team spent three months sorting out the implications of the entire strategic force modernization plan, against the background of real domestic political pressure for arms control and lack of perceived progress in the US-Soviet Strategic Arms Reduction Talks (START).

While the Scowcroft Report broadly endorsed the five-part strategic force modernization plan, the MX issue remained as contentious as it had always been. The report recommended, in the short term, that 100 MX should be deployed in existing Minuteman and Titan silos. Although they would remain vulnerable, in the medium term the other arms of the defence triad were deemed sufficient to deter the only means available to the Soviet Union to ensure the destruction of the US ICBM force—a surprise first strike.

Reasons *for* deploying the MX are set against the whole framework of the US-Soviet strategic balance. The deployment of counterforce-capable ICBMs, it was thought, would threaten the key Soviet assets, hardened command and control facilities, and rival missile silos. It would thus redress 'the strategic imbalance caused by the Soviet ability to destroy hardened land-based targets—with more than 600 newly deployed SS-18 and SS-19 ICBMs—while the United States is clearly not able to do so with its existing ballistic missile force.' Furthermore, cancelling MX after $5 billion had been spent on it would not 'communicate to the Soviets that we have the will essential to effective deterrence.'

MX was technically and militarily necessary because, the report concluded, Soviet advances in antiballistic missile technology might eventually confound attack by anything but a very large missile well equipped with penetration aids. The Air Force Ballistic Missile Office has a programme to equip MX with a 'defence suppression weapon', an onboard missile, launched in the terminal phase, which would attack antiballistic missile defence radars. Very significantly also, an MX force would be necessary to act as emergency military boosters to effect the patching of a strategic satellite network (*see* page 180). Sole reliance on the Space Shuttle was considered too dangerous.

These were the imperatives behind the deployment of at least 100 MX missiles. The report recommended a programme to demonstrate the feasibility and military value of superhardened silos.

However, the Scowcroft Commission also focused its attention very closely on the issue of arms control. It recognized that warheads, not launchers, should be the accounting unit for negotiation on strategic arms reduction (*see* Chapter Two), to give 'each side an incentive to move towards more stable and less vulnerable deployments.'

The ten-warhead MX, of course, runs counter to this principle, but was deemed necessary for the reasons already outlined and to offset the perceived

A Peacekeeper missile is punched out of its test stand by a gas generator just before the first-stage motor ignites. The first test flight was in June 1983 from Vandenberg AFB, California, and the unarmed missile covered over 7500 km.

Soviet advantage in very large multiple-warhead SS-18 and SS-19 ICBMs. There was a way out, however, and, typical of US practice, it involved the development of yet another weapons system. It meant moving to a small single-warhead launcher which would bring military and diplomatic advantages. The new missile was immediately nicknamed 'Midgetman'. It has also been referred to as 'Armadillo' and 'Small Intercontinental Missile' (SICM).

Midgetman

The Scowcroft Commission argued that having ten warheads on a single launcher invites attack. The Commission's case for a small weapon with a throw-weight of 1000 lb, compared with the Minuteman III's 2500 lb and the MX's 8300 lb, turns on the idea that a single-warhead ICBM denies the attacker the opportunity to destroy more than one warhead with one attacking warhead. Small size also greatly assists the task of finding different ways to achieve secure basing. Further, the Commission concluded that such a small missile could be hardened against the effects of a nuclear explosion using current technology, and would have enough destructive force and accuracy to threaten military targets at the other end. The Commission wanted full-scale development of Midgetman by 1987 (with operational capability in 1992), together with research into various basing modes, including hardened mobile shelters. The

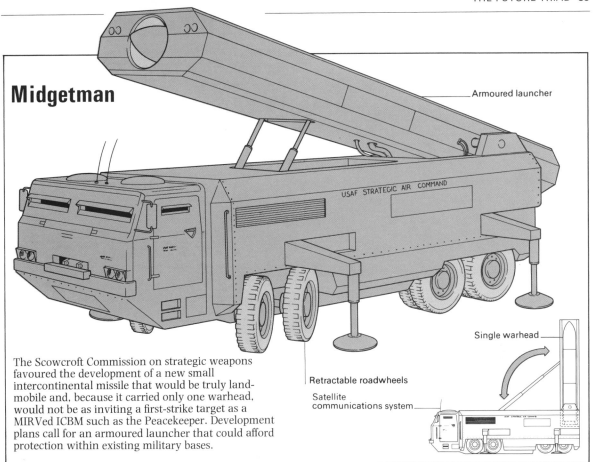

Midgetman

Armoured launcher

USAF STRATEGIC AIR COMMAND

Single warhead

Retractable roadwheels

Satellite communications system

The Scowcroft Commission on strategic weapons favoured the development of a new small intercontinental missile that would be truly land-mobile and, because it carried only one warhead, would not be as inviting a first-strike target as a MIRVed ICBM such as the Peacekeeper. Development plans call for an armoured launcher that could afford protection within existing military bases.

deployment of Midgetman *and* MX would be a breach of the unratified SALT II accords, which prohibit the development and testing of more than one new ICBM by either the Soviet Union or the United States.

Trident II
The Commission on Strategic Forces also extended the 'small is beautiful' concept to the ballistic missile submarine force. It recommended that research 'begins now on smaller submarines, each carrying fewer missiles than the Trident's 24, as a potential follow-on to the Trident force'. It cited the vulnerability of a large number of warheads grouped on a small number of platforms and the implications of Soviet progress in anti-submarine warfare. Trident II is, of course, the system that the British Conservative government has stated its commitment to acquire.

By late 1983 three *Ohio*-class SSBNs were at sea, armed with 24 Trident I missiles each. Seven more *Ohios* were on order, to enter service at the rate of one a year. A follow-on missile, called Trident II or D-5, is under development by Lockheed. It will utilize the full volume of the tubes on Trident submarines and will have a range greater than 7000 km without loss of payload. Further-improved accuracy and the Mk 12A warhead would give this sea-based missile a hard-target kill counterforce capability. In fact, the US Navy has requested additional funds, in order to be able to fit the D-5 with W-87 warheads, each with a yield of 475 kilotons, capable of crushing a silo hardened to 7200 psi. Engineering development was scheduled to start in 1984, with deployment by the end of the decade.

Cruise
This chapter is concerned with the strategic forces of the United States—nuclear-weapon delivery systems ultimately based in, and operationally commanded from, the United States itself. The cruise missile blurs this distinction, as it does so much else to shake the existing framework of deterrence. Cruise comes in three variations—air-, sea- and land-based. Ground-launched cruise missiles (GLCMs) have to be forward-based in European NATO countries to reach their designated targets. The political impact of cruise and its command and control systems are analysed in detail in Chapter Six. Meanwhile, the development and technical history of ground-launched cruise missiles, along with sea- and air-launched counterparts, are recorded here.

The cruise missile concept is an air-breathing, terrain-hugging, long-range penetration missile that flies to its target with great accuracy at low level, confounding traditional air defences. It is much smaller than a manned aircraft, and more manoeuvrable—or at least it should be.

The idea is an old one. The V-1s that the Luftwaffe used to attack London in 1944 were cruise missiles,

Far left: A Trident I C-4 submarine-launched ballistic missile fires its first-stage boost motor. The Trident has longer range than the Poseidon SLBM it is supplanting but equivalent accuracy, derived from the smaller and lighter Mk 5 guidance computer. The Mk 5 adds to the all-inertial Poseidon Mk 3 the refinement of stellar referencing. The post-boost vehicle, which is like a mini-spacecraft carrying the nuclear-armed re-entry vehicles, takes a star shot in the post-boost phase to fine-tune the trajectory. Eight 100-kiloton Mk 5 RVs are carried and Mk 500 Evader manoeuvring RV is being developed as an option. The Trident I is compatible with back-fitted Poseidon submarines and the much larger *Ohio* class has been designed around it.

The missile is launched and punched up to the surface by gas pressure. The first-stage motor is ignited in the air and the nose 'aerospike' is deployed, developing a supersonic shock wave which improves aerodynamic performance, but keeps down the missile's length. Its range is approximately 7400 km, virtually twice that of Poseidon, vastly increasing the sea-room in which Trident boats can patrol.

Below left: USS *Ohio* on sea trials. The *Ohio* class has a crew of 16 officers and 148 enlisted men. Six of these huge warships have been named: *Ohio, Michigan, Florida, Georgia, Rhode Island* and *Alabama*, taking over the names of states of the union previously allotted to US Navy battleships. The availability of each submarine is expected to be 65–70% and each will have two crews working on a schedule of 70 days on patrol and 25 days in dock. Overhauls and reactor core change will be at nine-year intervals. **Below:** USS *Ohio* fitting out at Groton, Connecticut, shows off her 24 Trident launch tubes. There were extensive delays and quality shortfalls during the construction of the first of the class.

Sea-basing was the original rationale for the new generation of cruise missiles when development started in 1972. A decade later air- and ground-launched versions are entering service, as the air force got in early on the act, ALCM development starting in 1973 and GLCMs in 1977.
Meanwhile the original 'slickem' concept turns virtually any US warship into a strategic launch platform, but particularly nuclear-powered attack submarines whose primary role was previously to act as anti-submarine warfare platforms themselves. The picture sequence shows the first operational test of the conventional warhead anti-ship SLCM striking the target after launch from a submerged submarine over 140 km away. The first operational land attack and anti-ship SLCMs were embarked in the USS *Guitarro* in Aug. 1982.

pilotless aircraft powered by a pulse-jet engine, in contrast to the German army's V-2 ballistic rockets. V-1s could be stopped by anti-aircraft gunfire or shot down by piston-engined fighters. V-2s were completely and terrifyingly unstoppable.

The United States and the Soviet Union developed a range of cruise-type missiles in the 1950s. The Americans concentrated on strategic systems such as the Mace and Matador, based in Europe, and the intercontinental Snark—all of which were rendered obsolete by the development of ICBMs. The Soviet Union concentrated on short-range tactical systems which remain effective today, particularly in sea warfare. Meanwhile, cruise missile developments were outside the Strategic Arms Limitation Talks (SALT) accords of the 1970s.

With the US defence establishment agonizing over the future of the manned bomber throughout that decade, research was maturing on separate but interlocking technologies—small, fuel-efficient engines that could propel a tiny airframe over great distances and highly sophisticated navigational techniques that could follow a computer-predicted course low over satellite-mapped terrain. The system was called TERCOM ('terrain counter-matching'), which would update inertial guidance to produce superlative accuracy. TERCOM is pure mathematics. Satellite mapping of hills, lakes and forests is turned into a digital code of numbers. The cruise missile's down-pointing radar reads the real terrain over which it passes and its computer compares it with the number code. This has not always worked on test flights and it will be clear that apparently cheap cruise

missiles need the resources of a superpower space programme to make them work.

When the B-1 bomber was cancelled by President Carter in 1977 a Joint Cruise Missile Project office was set up by the Department of Defense to bring together the disparate programmes then under way—Boeing's air-launched weapon and General Dynamic's Tomahawk sea- and ground-launched missiles. The range of programmes, missions and methods of basing is summarized below.

Air-launched missiles

Boeing AGM-86B ALCM

Approximate speed	550 mph (885 km/h)
Warhead	Nuclear W80-1
Range	1550 n.mi. (2870 km)
Propulsion	Williams F107-101

The original requirement was for 3418 missiles between the fiscal years 1980 and 1987. Flyaway cost per missile is approximately $1 million. In Feb. 1983 it was announced that production would halt when 1500 had been manufactured, to be followed by Mark II ALCM with a greater range and some 'stealth' qualities. The first ALCMs were operational on B-52Gs at Griffiss AFB, New York, in Dec. 1982. Full operational capability was planned for 1985 when 104 aircraft would be loaded, each with 12 ALCMs mounted externally, based at Wurtsmith AFB, Michigan, Grand Forks AFB, North Dakota, and Ellsworth AFB, South Dakota.

The guidance is inertial, with the addition of TERCOM.

General Dynamics AGM 109H

A USAF Medium-Range Air-Surface Missile (MRASM), it is a conventionally tipped air-launched missile for attacking high-priority targets, or dispensing sub-munitions for airfield attack. Based on the Tomahawk cruise missile, it is non-strategic.

General Dynamics AGM 109L
A US Navy air-launched missile with conventional dual-purpose warhead for carrier-based strikes on land or warship targets, it is non-strategic.

Sea-launched missiles
The General Dynamics Tomahawk was designed originally around the 21-in US Navy torpedo tube for launch from submarines. It has evolved into a range of systems, including the very important ground-launched variation on the original theme. Under development since 1972, the SLCM (or 'slickem') has given the greatest trouble in its technical development, causing several organizational shakeups and constant rescheduling of the programme.

Because SLCMs can be mounted on virtually any reasonably sized vessel, either above or below the water, they have very significant implications for attempts at arms control.

General Dynamics BGM-109A

Approximate speed	550 mph (885 km/h)
Warhead	Nuclear W-80, 200 KT
Range	1550 n.mi. (2870 km)
Propulsion	Williams F107-400 turbofan

This is a nuclear strategic attack version which could reach Moscow from launch west of the Hebrides. Guidance is by TERCOM, but because it first flies over open sea, the missile must first reach a pre-mapped coastal entry point under inertial guidance before TERCOM takes over. Deployment is scheduled for mid-1984.

BGM-109C
This has a shorter range (1500 km) than the strategic version and is equipped with a conventional warhead for attacking small land targets. Guidance is by TERCOM but with an electro-optical system for terminal homing. It is non-strategic.

BGM-109B
This is an anti-ship version with a conventional warhead and a range of 240 n.mi. (450 km). Because TERCOM cannot work on open sea, it has an inertial guidance system, with an active radar seeker for terminal homing.

The first conventional versions of the Tomahawk SLCM entered trial service late in 1982 — even after the Congressional General Accounting Office had published a report raising doubts as to their effectiveness. Nevertheless, the 4000 SLCMs which the US Navy intends to acquire will be based on a very wide range of platforms. *Sturgeon* and *Los Angeles* class nuclear-powered attack submarines will take them to sea and the *Los Angeles* class will be fitted with 12-round vertical launch tubes. SLCMs will also be mounted on *Spruance* class destroyers, Aegis air-defence cruisers, the nuclear-powered *Long Beach Virginia* and *California* class cruisers, and aboard the old battleships of the *Iowa* class, put into commission again and equipped with armoured deck launchers for the new missiles.

Ground-launched cruise missiles
The GLCM, which is the backbone of the modernization plans for the intermediate nuclear force in Europe (*see* page 152), is derived from and very similar to, the US Navy's sea-launched missile. On launch from the transporter-erector-launcher vehicle (TEL), a solid-fuel rocket engine boosts the missile to cruising speed. The booster is then jettisoned, fins and wings flip out, the main engine's inlet deploys and the turbofan ignites.

General Dynamics AGM 109G

Approximate speed	550 mph (885 km/h)
Warhead	Nuclear W84 200 KT
Range	1550 n.mi. (2870 km)
Propulsion	Williams F-107-400
Guidance	Inertial plus TERCOM

Sea-launched cruise missiles

The variety of sea platforms from which cruise missiles can be launched is very wide. Armoured deck launchers on surface warships will eventually be replaced by vertical launch systems below deck, while a similar system will be built into new attack submarines of the *Los Angeles* class. **Far left:** A Tomahawk launch from the destroyer USS *Merrill*. **Left:** A submarine-launched Tomahawk breaks surface. **Above:** Tomahawk launch from USS *New Jersey* in mid-1983. **Right:** A *Los Angeles*-class nuclear-powered attack submarine. Every such boat equipped with Tomahawk has a strategic nuclear land attack capability.

MIRVing the Bomber Force

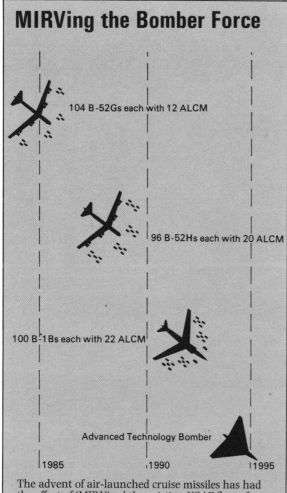

104 B-52Gs each with 12 ALCM

96 B-52Hs each with 20 ALCM

100 B-1Bs each with 22 ALCM

Advanced Technology Bomber

1985 | 1990 | 1995

The advent of air-launched cruise missiles has had the effect of 'MIRVing' the existing USAF fleet of B-52s in the same way that ICBMs are able to make attacks on multiple targets with a single launcher.

B-52s which, on previous plans, had to smash their way through air defences with Short-Range Attack Missiles (SRAMs), can now stand off and launch attacks at multiple targets 2500 km away.

On current plans 90 of the B-52G fleet will be modified to carry 12 ALCMs and are expected to revert to conventional and maritime roles in the late 1980s if their airframes can stand the strain. Meanwhile, the 90-strong B-52H force will continue in the penetration role, armed with SRAMs and free-fall bombs. Starting in 1986 as the first B-1Bs become available, the B-52Hs will in turn be converted to carry up to 20 ALCMs. The B-52Hs are planned to serve well into the 1990s as ALCM carriers, while the B-1B takes over the penetration role until the Advanced Technology Bomber (ATB or 'stealth' aircraft) in turn relieves it to become an ALCM carrier and strategic power projection aircraft with conventional weapons.

Right: US Air Force armourers at Griffiss AFB load a pylon of AGM-86B ALCMs to the wing of a B-52G. Each one has a 200-kiloton warhead. Meanwhile an advanced air-launch cruise missile (AALCM) is under development.

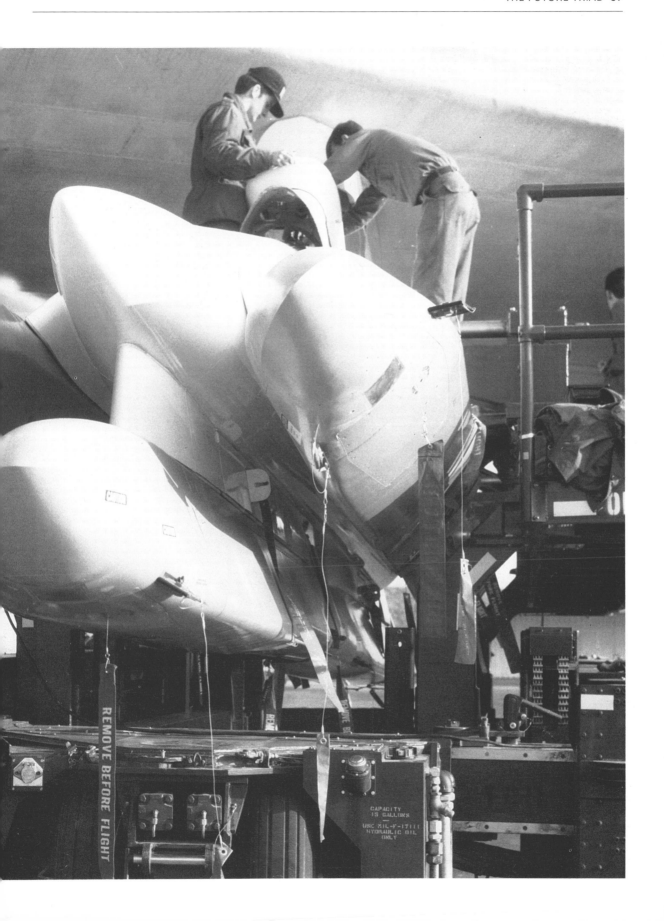

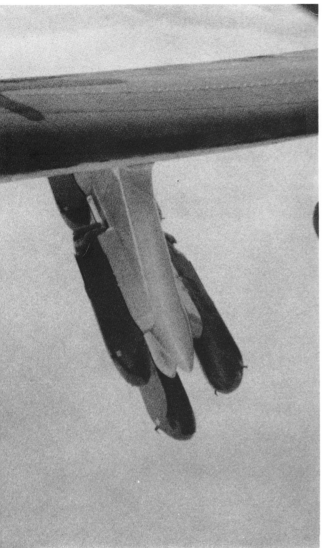

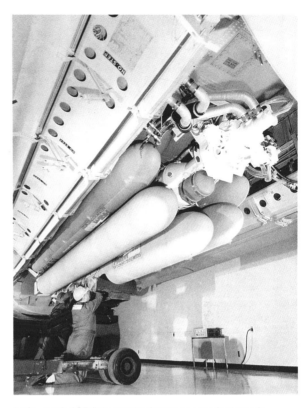

Left: A KC-135 flying tanker boom operator's view of a thirsty B-52G taking on fuel. The load of twelve ALCMs is clearly visible. The white shades in the cockpit glazing are anti-nuclear flash shutters. **Above:** After intense competition, Boeing's AGM-86 beat the General Dynamics' Tomahawk for the air-launched cruise missile contract. However, the AGM-109 ALCM (seen above in a B-52 bomb bay mock-up) lives on as the USAF's AGM-109H or Medium Range Air-to-Surface Missile (MRASM). The payload can be airfield-cratering sub-munitions and the stand-off range more than 500 km. **Below:** Boeing AGM-86B ALCM, wings, fins and turbofan inlet deployed. The range is 2800 km plus.

Cruise missile operation

Air-, sea- and ground-launched cruise missiles actually function in similar ways. Air-launched missiles are dropped from the launch aircraft, whereas land- and sea-based missiles are punched out of their launchers by a solid-propellant rocket motor before the turbofan engine fires and the wings and control surfaces deploy, 14 seconds into the flight.

The missile is now on its way under inertial guidance to the initial timing control point (ITCP), first arcing up in a high trajectory, then coming down as low as 50 ft at the pre-mapped ITCP. The missile now flies a pre-charted course, following the terrain, skirting round known defence sites and carrying out a series of time-controlled manoeuvres, flying in straight lines between turning points. The missile's radar altimeter meanwhile 'reads' sections of terrain over which it is passing and compares them digitally with the satellite-mapped computer code. By taking multiple fixes over each TERCOM field and by using a computer 'voting' technique, the system can locate a position other than the centre of the map or map cell and thus make its own corrections. On quoted test performance, the technique enables the guidance system to fix a navigational position with the probability of an error less than one part in 10 million. It needs a total of 24 flight events to create a warhead arm, and final arming only takes place during the terminal manoeuvre to the target, which can be made from any direction.

What is cruise for? Although it is not certain that the full programmes will be completed, the United States may procure 10,000 or more of the various versions—at least half of them nuclear-tipped. The deployment in Europe of GLCMs has major political implications, but what is the military reasoning behind a weapon that takes several hours to reach its target and is vulnerable, as manned aircraft are vulnerable, to tactical air defence?

As we have seen, the very existence of the interlocking technology behind cruise was a strong incentive to see if the idea would work. Once the technology had been proven and demonstrated in two distinct programmes, both the US Navy and the USAF wrote complex military requirements around it —weapons research has a dynamic all of its own.

The requirement for the ALCM as stated in the Department of Defense's Annual Report to Congress, Fiscal Year 1983, is to 'redress the strategic imbalance relatively quickly . . . the presence of a larger number of cruise missiles would saturate enemy air defences increasing the survivability of our penetrating bombers'. Another way of reading this is that cruise-missile deployment is simply to force the Soviet Union to allot vast resources to creating an air defence capable of dealing with cruise missile attack. This means airborne warning and control aircraft, high-performance interceptors equipped with look-down, shoot-down radars and missiles, new SAM belts, and even decoy landscapes. James Wade, a former US Under Secretary of Defence, estimated that it might cost the Soviet Union $100 billion to stop cruise— money that might have been spent on antisubmarine warfare, for example.

Bomber force modernization

The ALCM and the follow-on advanced air-launched cruise missile to be built by General Dynamics are the key to US bomber force modernization. Further, all B-52Gs and Hs will be fitted with a new Offensive Avionics System (OAS) and some will be specially hardened against the effects of electromagnetic pulse (EMP) and will carry improved electronic counter-measures equipment. The USAF has requested appropriation for a $1 billion programme to produce a common strategic rotary launcher (CSRL) to accommodate ALCMs, SRAMs and free-fall bombs on B-52s, B-1Bs and the so-called 'stealth' bomber.

In spite of the huge investment in cruise, the manned, penetrating bomber is still central to force modernization plans and, if anything, this programme has been even more controversial. It is called the Rockwell International B-1B.

When the B-1 bomber, under development from the late 1960s, was cancelled by President Carter in June 1977 the stated reasons were cost, the effectiveness of the ALCM in doing the same job more cheaply and the projected inability of the B-1 to penetrate Soviet air defences. When in Oct. 1981 President Reagan announced plans to build 100 B-1Bs he was fulfilling a long-standing political promise and, by the end of the year, Congress had approved the plans, after intense lobbying by the manufacturers and by the USAF who argued that maintaining the B-52 fleet to the end of the century would cost as much as the $100 billion bill for a new long-range combat aircraft force.

Part of the political debate hinged on the allocation of resources between the B-1B and the advanced technology bomber (ATB), the so-called 'stealth' aircraft which, it was envisaged, would enter service in the early 1990s. It was planned, moreover, that the ATB should then take over the B-1B's role as a manned penetrating bomber, leaving the B-1B to continue as an ALCM carrier and strategic power-projection aircraft.

B-1B

Partisans of the B-1 programme say that the USAF needs a manned penetrating bomber to achieve complete and flexible target coverage of the Soviet Union. Moreover, because it can carry all sorts of countermeasures—plus, of course, human beings—it can confound and get through defences that the ALCM cannot.

There are doubts—and not just about the programme's huge expense. In the first hearing the Secretary of Defense, Caspar Weinberger, stated that the B-1B would be able to penetrate Soviet air defences until 1990. Then he revised this statement to 'well into the 1990s'.

There have been many proposals and efforts made to keep Strategic Air Command's fleets of B-52s flying into the 1990s and beyond. Airframe re-engineering and intensive avionics retrofits have kept the ageing warhorses going, the aircraft themselves now often older than the pilots who fly them. One often considered proposal is re-engining, with big high-bypass turbofans replacing the eight thirsty turbojets of 1950s vintage. Unlike the re-engining of the KC-135 fleet, however, this is not yet official policy.

The B-1B is designed to do this in three ways. It has variable-geometry wings, set forward for takeoffs from runways much shorter than those required for B-52 operations, but swept back for low-level flight at high subsonic speed. Shorter takeoff allows B-1B operations from widely dispersed airfields, thus increasing the force's ability to survive. The aircraft can approach its target fast at low level, coming in under the radar, jinking and bucking around hills and valleys using terrain-following radar.

The B-1B has a radar cross-section of around 10 sq ft, 0·1% that of a B-52, but the big airframe is packed with electronics. The Boeing Military Airplane Company provides the offensive avionics system which includes forward-looking and terrain-following radar, an extremely accurate inertial navigation system and doppler radar altimeter, and, in addition, a highly sophisticated navigation and weapon delivery system. Also on board is AFSATCOM satellite communication equipment.

Defensive avionics are built round the AN/ALQ-

161 electronic countermeasures system developed by Eaton Corporation's AIL Division, which controls a large number of jamming transmitters and antennae. These generate 'jamming chains' around the periphery of the aircraft to jam signals coming from hostile radars. A separate network of antennae, receivers and processors act as the 'ears' of the AN/ALQ 31, picking up and identifying new signals and directing jamming operations. On stated USAF figures the AN/ALQ-161 consumes 120 kw of power in an 'all out' jamming mode—'this is equivalent to 120 microwave ovens cooking meals at once.'

There is also the ALQ-153 tail-warning system and, if all else fails, the ALQ-161 will launch radar-blinding chaff clouds or flares to draw off a heat-seeking missile attack. The differences between the B-1B and the original B-1, of which four prototypes were built, are hard to distinguish externally. The internal structure will be strengthened to increase the gross takeoff weight from 395,000 lb to 477,000 lb (more than that of the B-52), and the B-1's crew-escape capsules have been replaced by ejector seats. The variable-geometry engine inlets, which pushed up the cost so much on the B-1 programme but allowed Mach 2 speeds, will be replaced by fixed inlets optimized for the B-1B's low level, subsonic penetration mission. The first B-1B is scheduled to fly in 1985 and enter service with SAC in 1986, with a 100-strong force available by the end of the decade.

The fourth B-1 prototype flying with wings forward in the low-speed position. This prototype had full offensive and defensive avionics installed.

Advanced technology bomber

The ATB relies on deception rather than speed and high-powered airborne jammers to outwit its opponents. It is designed so as to present the lowest possible optical, radar and heat (infrared) signatures to hostile sensors. A technology demonstrator has been under development at the famous Lockheed Skunk works at Burbank, California, which produced the U-2 and SR-71, and a twin-engined prototype is reported to have flown for the first time in 1977.

The technology demonstrator, prototype, X-25, has high-mounted engines, heat-suppression devices and a carefully shaped airframe, eliminating as many radar echo-producing corners as possible and incorporating much non-metallic composite materials. Kevlar-like coatings are supposed to be able to absorb radar emissions. Lockheed is building perhaps two dozen F-19 'stealth' reconnaissance and fighter aircraft for the USAF, while Northrop is developing the ATB.

Main picture: A KC-135R testbed aircraft, re-engined with fuel-efficient turbofan engines, refuels an original KC-135 of Strategic Air Command in flight. The USAF operates over 600 flying tankers and re-engining will keep a proportion of them in the air into the next century. **Right:** The second of the four original B-1 prototypes (first flown in 1974) was reworked in 1982 as a testbed for the B-1B. It was modified to simulate the new aircraft's flight-handling qualities, in order to test stability and control and weapons separation. **Below:** An often-proposed solution to US bomber force modernization was the development of a stretched F-111H with strategic range and carrying a larger number of B-61 bombs or SRAMs. The project was effectively axed in 1979.

US Free-Fall Bombs and Nuclear Warhead Designation

Official US government figures count the stockpile of nuclear warheads of all sorts as it stands now in the 'low tens of thousands'. Independent sources put the figure at around 30,000, roughly divided equally between tactical and strategic weapons, in contrast to the high point of 32,000 warheads in 1967 when large numbers of tactical weapons swelled the numbers. As with delivery systems, warheads themselves are replaced and modernized. Four types of nuclear weapon are being withdrawn from the US arsenal: atomic landmines, Nike Hercules SAMs, B53 strategic free-fall bombs and Titan II nine-megaton warheads. Ten more types will be replaced, including artillery shells and three others partially replaced. However, the number of new warheads now in production for systems such as the W78 Minuteman III warhead, the W80 cruise missile series and W70 Mod 3 ER enhanced-radiation warhead for the Lance missile could total 9000 new warheads. Fourteen more types are in development to be produced during 1983-7. More are planned in the late 1980s, and independent sources estimate that an additional 15,000 nuclear warheads will be produced for these future weapon systems by 1990. The total number of warheads could grow to 32,000 by 1990, requiring significant increases in plutonium production.

Mk 17	First US thermonuclear weapon. Obsolete.
B28	Tactical and strategic free-fall bomb. Deployed on B-52 (4-8), F-4 (1), A-4 (1), A-6 (3), B-1B (up to 20). Strategic bomb yields up to 1·45 megatons.
Mk 36	Strategic bomb. Obsolete.
Mk 39	Large strategic bomb. Parachute retarded. Obsolete.
B41	Strategic bomb. Obsolete.
B43	Tactical and strategic free-fall configured in several yields up to megaton range. Deployed on A-6 (3), A-4 (1), A-7 (4), F-16 (2), F-4 (3), F-111 (6), B-52 (4). Parachute-retarded for air burst or free-fall (B43Y1). Also delayed surface burst from release at low altitude.
B53	Strategic bomb, being withdrawn.
B57	Tactical weapon. Mods 0/1/2 have yields from 10 to 20 kilotons. Deployed on A-4 (1), A-6 (3), A-7 (4), P-3 (3), S-3 (3), SH-3 (1), F-16 (2), F-4 (3), FB-111 (6).
B61	Tactical and strategic bomb. Mods 0, 2, 3, 4, 5 have yields from 100 to 500 kilotons. Mod 1 has yield in megaton range. Mods 1, 3, 4 classified as strategic.
B77	Development programme for new bomb with full fusing option. Free-fall, retarded, air- or ground-burst with aerofoil parachute.
B83	Development programme for new strategic free-fall bomb, variable yield up to 1 megaton.
BDU8, 11, 12, 38	Training versions of nuclear weapons.
Mk 43	Nuclear depth charge.
Mk 57	Nuclear depth charge 5-10 kilotons.
Mk 101	Nuclear depth charge 5-10 kilotons.
Mk 104	Nuclear weapon.

Missile-delivered warheads

W25	Warhead for Genie AAM, 1·25-kiloton yield.
W30	Warhead for TALOS shipborne SAM. Five-kiloton yield, obsolete.
W31	Nuclear warhead for Nike-Hercules SAM, withdrawing.
W44	Nuclear depth charge warhead for ASROC, 1-kiloton yield.
W45 (Mod 1)	Nuclear warhead for Terrier naval shipborne SAM, 1-kiloton yield.
W50	Nuclear warhead for Pershing Ia, 60/200/400-kiloton yield.
W53	Nuclear warhead for Titan II, 9-megaton yield, being withdrawn.
W54	Atomic landmine, 0·1-kiloton, being withdrawn.
W55	Nuclear depth charge for Subroc, 1-kiloton yield.
W58	Nuclear warhead for Polaris A-3 SLBM, 150-kiloton yield, obsolete.
W62	Nuclear warhead for Minuteman III, 200-kiloton yield.
W68	Nuclear warhead for Poseidon SLBM, 40-kiloton yield.
W69	Nuclear warhead for SRAM, 200-kiloton yield.
W70 (Mod 1/2)	Nuclear warhead for Lance SSM, 1-100-kiloton yield.
W70 (Mod 3)	Nuclear warhead for Lance (ER).
W72	Nuclear warhead for Walleye.
W75	Nuclear warhead for 8-in AFAP.
W76	Nuclear warhead for Mk 4 RV on Trident SLBM, 100-kiloton yield.
W78	Nuclear warhead for Minuteman III ICBM, 330-kiloton yield.
W79	Nuclear warhead for 8-in AFAP (ER).
W80	Nuclear warhead series for cruise missiles.
W80-0	Nuclear warhead for BGM 109A SLCM, 200-kiloton yield.
W80-1	Nuclear warhead for AGM-86B ALCM, 200-kiloton yield.
W81	Nuclear warhead for Standard SM-2, shipborne SAM, 1-kiloton yield.
W82	Nuclear warhead for 155 mm AFAP.
W84	Nuclear warhead for BGM 109 GLCM, 200-kiloton yield.
W85	Nuclear warhead for Pershing II SSM, airburst, 40-kiloton yield.
W86	Nuclear warhead for Pershing II SSM, earth-penetrator.
W87	Nuclear warhead for Peacekeeper.

Command, Control and Communications (C3)

A very important component of the strategic force modernization programme concerns C3. The overall budget allocation for the fiscal year 1984 is $34·7 billion, that is 8·5 billion more than the previous year, reflecting the growing importance of military command, control and communications. The great fear is that of 'decapitation', literally, lopping the decision-making head off the strategic forces of the United States, leaving the massively armed limbs unable to respond. This is not just a question of eliminating the President and his staff wherever they might be. Electromagnetic pulse (see page 23) will simply burn out traditional means of communication and the emphasis is on EMP—'hardening' by extensive use of fibre optics—and by double routing. When this does not work the USAF's Electronic Systems Division (ESD) is simply, in their own words, resorting to 'brute force', by sealing equipment, such as SAC's ground-based emergency action systems, in steel and concrete, and by providing filters to block off potential EMP penetration paths through antennae and similar gatherers.

The early warning system will be upgraded by the introduction of a new satellite system, codenamed Aquarius, which will transmit data to mobile ground terminals. The ground-based radars screening the United States will be upgraded, as already described, while research and development continues on a next-generation advanced missile warning system to replace or augment the satellite system in the 1990s. A series of satellite-borne radars screening low-level approach to the United States over the North Pole are also under consideration. There are, in addition, plans to install a network of sensors, called the Integrated Operational Nuclear Detection Detonation Detecting System (IONDS), on the satellites of the NAVSTAR global positioning system (see page 180), which will provide the means to detect a nuclear detonation anywhere in the world.

Communications

The operations of existing US strategic communications networks are looked at in Chapter Three. Upgrading of capabilities is a very important component of the strategic forces modernization plan and the various programmes underway are examined here.

Air Force Satellite Communication System (AFSATCOM)
AFSATCOM Phase I is in service. 'Host' geostationary satellites of the Defense Satellite Communication System already in place are equipped with single-channel transponders and used to communicate via UHF (ultra high frequency) with certain SIOP units equipped with special terminals, including some B-52s, EC-135 control aircraft, F-111As, SAC Minuteman control centres and TACAMO aircraft communicating with SSBNs. Phase II, under development, will give the system greater ability to survive

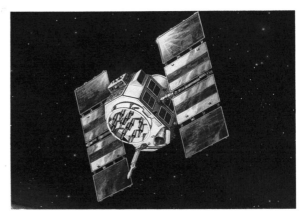
The Navstar navigation satellite. It will carry the IONDS system. The Soviet equivalent is called Glonass.

and make it more jam-resistant, while Phase III, now in the concept stage, is working to a 'common transmission format for maximum interoperability among all services'.

MILSTAR
MILSTAR is a programme at the planning stage for an EHF (extremely high frequency) satellite communications system highly resistant to jamming, with secure voice and data transmission capability. It is a joint service programme, whose principal users would be nuclear forces, whether Army, Navy or Air Force. MILSTAR, when operational, may possibly replace the Navy's fleet satellite communication system (FLSATCOM) and the Air Force's AFSATCOM, which are judged to be relatively open to attack or disruption.

A programme called SACDIN (SAC digital network) is related to the updates of the AFSATCOM and MILSTAR programmes. SACDIN, which should go into production in 1984, would modernize SAC's C³ systems, providing rapid two-way command and control information between SAC HQ and operational elements, such as missile-launch centres and aircraft already airborne.

Ground-based communicating systems
GWEN (Ground Wave Emergency Network) is a programme for hardening elements of the MEECN (minimum essential emergency communications network) within the United States. Its primary task is to retain control over SAC's bomber fleet even when under attack by nuclear weapons and blanketed by EMP effects. The system aims to negate EMP by using a very low frequency ground wave, which is generally capable of resisting disruptions in the ionosphere.

In its second phase GWEN is to develop a large number of alternative paths to ensure that messages would get through even if large sections of the grid were destroyed. This plan calls for up to 300 GWEN relay sites or 'nodes' rather than the original 40 or so planned for the initial or thin-line section of the programme designed for completion by 1985. The full GWEN plan is estimated to cost nearly $3 billion.

B-1B Defensive and Offensive Avionics Systems

Contractor: Rockwell International, North American
Aircraft Operations
Powerplant: 4 × General Electric F101-GE-102
turbofans, each 30,000 lb thrust
Crew: Four (pilot, co-pilot and two systems operators)
Dimensions: span 137 ft (41·67 m); (fully swept) 78 ft
(23·84 m); length 147 ft (45·78 m); height 34 ft (10·36 m).

Weight: Maximum takeoff weight 477,000 lb
(214,000 kg)
Performance: Maximum speed high subsonic at low level,
supersonic at altitude
Range (unrefuelled) intercontinental
Armament: 125,000 lb of free-fall bombs or 38 SRAMs
(short-range attack missiles) or 22 ALCMS.

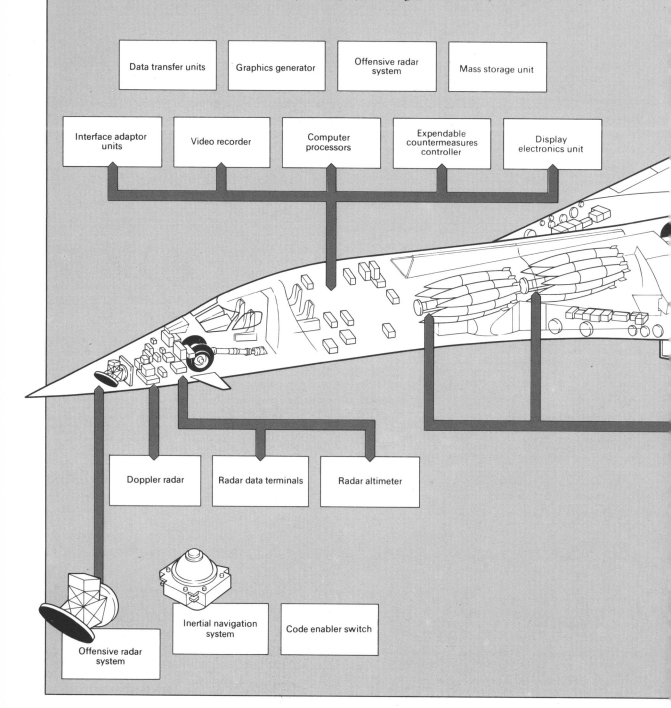

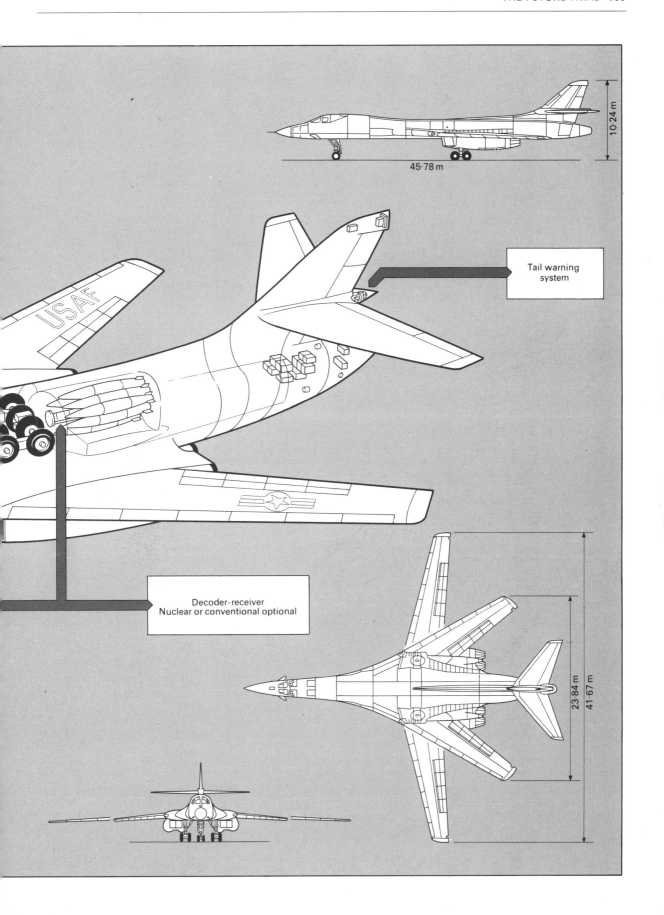

10·24 m

45·78 m

Tail warning
system

USAF

Decoder-receiver
Nuclear or conventional optional

23·84 m

41·67 m

Submarine communication systems

The ELF (extremely low frequency) concept for communicating with submerged submarines goes back to the late 1950s. Experimental transmissions began in 1969 but plans for operational systems, codenamed Sanguine and then Seafarers, came to a dead end.

There was, all the time, a test facility based at Clam Lake, Wisconsin, in the Chequamagon National Forest, with the task both of proving the technology and of establishing that ELF transmissions were not harmful to people or the environment. In 1976 the facility sent its first message through two 14-mile long antenna lines strung on poles like power lines and reached submarines equipped with experimental receivers in the Mediterranean and under the Arctic ice cap.

An ELF system consists of a power source and long antenna cables electrically grounded at both ends. The power source drives current through the cable into the ground. From that point the current returns deep through the earth to the electrical ground at the other end—thus forming a loop, with the earth itself providing one half of the circuit. The lower the conductivity of the earth, the deeper the shape of the loop and the shaping of the radio waves it will propagate to bounce off the ionosphere and move in stately progression around the globe. The geological formation of upper Michigan and northern Wisconsin, called the Laurentian Shield, is very dry granite with low conductivity, ideal for an operational military ELF site. However, the ELF plan has its drawbacks. The huge antennae are an obvious target for attack and there have been fears all along that the system would offer only marginal improvements. Moreover, an ELF transmission would take 15 minutes to send a three-letter code message.

In 1981 final plans for an operational ELF system were drawn up and approved by the President and a funding request of $230 million presented to Con-

The Boeing E-6 aircraft is on order for the US Navy and will fulfil the TACAMO role of airborne communication with submerged ballistic missile submarines. It is based on the E-3A Sentry AWACS airframe.

optical and laser-based means of communication. SAOCS is a research programme for an optical submarine-aircraft communication system and OSCAR is a programme for a satellite-based laser system. Radio frequency links would carry messages from aircraft or ground stations to a network of satellites, which would then use so-called 'blue-green' lasers to relay the messages to submerged submarines. The commitment to the ELF programme probably means that these alternative investigations will be discontinued.

Command Centres

The satellite, ground-based and mobile communications systems just described are supposed to link the decision-making 'brain' of the national command authority via the operational military commands to the SIOP forces, underground, at sea or in the air. It follows that equal, if not greater, efforts are being made to increase ability to survive at the top of the command tree as well as down its roots and branches. The first E-4B ABNCP (airborne national command post) became operational in 1980 and three more were to be in service by 1985, providing an airborne command platform for the President, the Secretary of Defense, the Joint Chiefs of Staff and CINCSAC, the Commander in Chief of Strategic Air Command.

The E-4B is based on the Boeing 747 airframe. Its enhanced capacity to survive, compared with the earlier E-4A, is provided by EMP-hardening, the ability to operate from shorter runways and the fact that it can fly longer and more flexible orbits because of its multi-directional satellite communications. A radome on top of the fuselage contains a stabilized antenna that is always pointing at a communications satellite which affords world-wide radio links using super high frequency (SHF). The E-4B is also fitted with high-powered and jam-resistant very low frequency (VLF) and low frequency (LF) equipment for direct communications with SIOP forces. Meanwhile, the EC-135 group, which provides airborne control of the Minuteman force and at least one of which is airborne at all times, is receiving updates and modifications to give it greater EMP-resistance and increase its transmitter power. SAC has put forward proposals for a new fleet of command-post aircraft based on the C-17 assault transport airframe.

Airborne command centres are important in what the Department of Defense blandly calls the 'transattack' phase, but they must land eventually. It is planned therefore to deploy 'terrestrial mobile command centres' (MCCs) to take over if airborne command posts have ceased to function. Meanwhile, the existing fixed command centres at NORAD and SAC headquarters, and the BMEWS sites at Thule, Clear and Fylingdales, are completing major electronic equipment update programmes.

gress. As it stands the plan calls for full activation of the Clam Lake site and activation of a new transmitter and a 56-mile antenna system stretching through state forests near KI Sawyer AFB, in the upper peninsula of Michigan.

The E-6 aircraft is scheduled to take over the TACAMO (take charge and move out) ballistic missile submarine airborne communication system role by the end of the 1980s with a squadron of the aircraft, based on the Boeing 707/C-135 airframe, deployed in the Pacific and the Atlantic.

Meanwhile disparate alternative research programmes on means of communicating with submerged submarines continue. Those that have had their existence declassified (but not much else) are the jam-resistant 'Gryphon' programme, the satellite-based 'Hydrus', the High-Volume Information Transfer Project and the Submarine-Integrated Communications Centre.

Research has been going on for a long time into

World Nuclear Delivery Systems

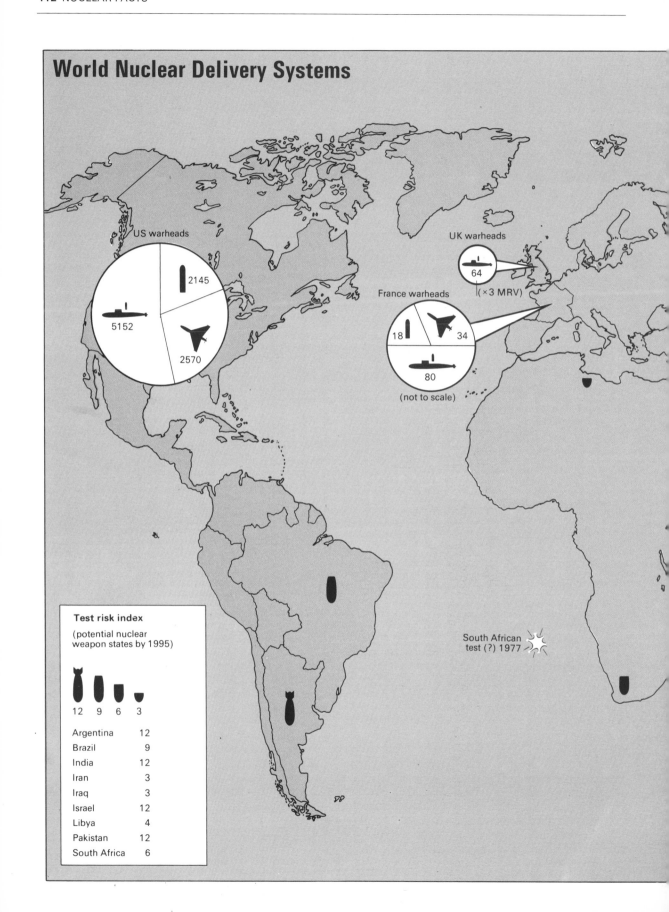

US warheads

2145

5152

2570

UK warheads

64

(×3 MRV)

France warheads

18

34

80

(not to scale)

South African
test (?) 1977

Test risk index

(potential nuclear
weapon states by 1995)

12 9 6 3

Argentina	12
Brazil	9
India	12
Iran	3
Iraq	3
Israel	12
Libya	4
Pakistan	12
South Africa	6

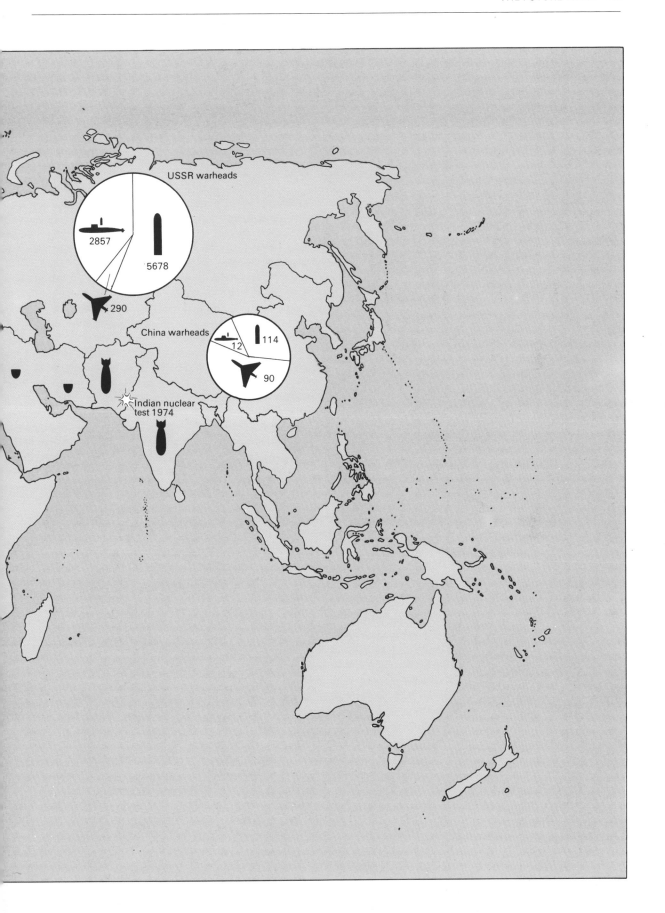

USSR warheads

2857

5678

290

China warheads

12

114

90

Indian nuclear
test 1974

World Nuclear Delivery Systems

US Strategic nuclear weapon delivery systems (end 1983)

Land-based ICBMs	Number Deployed	Number of Warheads	Warhead Total	Range (km)	Accuracy (CEP m)	Total MT delivery
Minuteman II	450	1×1/2 MT	450	11,300	370	540
Minuteman III	250	3×170 KT	750	13,000	280	128
Minuteman III (Mk 12A)	300	3×335 KT	900	12,000	220	302
Titan II (phasing out)	45	1×9 KT	45	15,000	1300	405
Sub total	*1045*		*2145*			*1375*
Sea-based SLBMs						
Poseidon C-3	304	10×50 KT	3040	4000	450	122
Trident I C-4	264	8×100 KT	2112	7400	450	211
Sub total	*568*		*5152*			*333*
Strategic Bombers (excludes 56 FB-111As)						
B-52D (phasing out)	31			9900		
B-52G	151	} 1140 SRAM, 200		12,000		
B-52H	90	} ALCM + free-fall bombs		16,000		
Sub total	*272*		*2570* (est)			*1745* (est)
TOTAL	**1885** delivery vehicles		**9867** warheads			**3453** MT

Soviet strategic nuclear weapon delivery systems (end 1983)

Land-based ICBMs	Number Deployed	Number of Warheads	Warhead Total	Range (km)	Accuracy (CEP m)	Total MT delivery
SS-11	260	1×1 MT	260	10,500	1400	260
SS-11 Mod 3	260	3×1-300 KT MRV	780	8,800	1100	260
SS-13	60	1×750 KT	60	10,000	2000	36
SS-17 Mod 2	30	1×6 MT	30	11,000	450	180
SS-17 Mod 1	} 120	4×750 KT/	} 480	10,000	450	} 360
SS-17 Mod 3		4×2 MT		10,000	–	
SS-18 Mod 1		1×20 MT		12,000	450	
SS-18 Mod 2	} 308	8×900 KT MIRV	} 2208	11,000	450	} 2795
SS-18 Mod 3		1×20 MT		10,500	350	
SS-18 Mod 4		10×500 KT MIRV		11,000	300	
SS-19 Mod 2	60	1×5 MT	60	10,000	300	600
SS-19 Mod 3	300	6×550 MT	1800	10,000	300	990
Sub total	*1398*		*5678*			*5481*
Sea-based SLBMs						
SS-N-5	48	1×1 MT	48	1400	2800	} 48
SS-N-6	} 384	1×1 MT	} 628	2400	900	} 250
SS-N-6 (MRV)		2×200 KT		3000	1400	
SS-N-8	289	1×800 KT/1 MT	289	7800	1300	231
SS-N-17	12	1×1 MT	12	3900	1500	9
SS-N-18	224	1/3/7×250 KT –1 MT MIRV	1680	6500	600	336
SS-NX-20	20	6–10 MIRV	200	8300	–	40
Sub total	*977*		*2857*			*914*
Strategic Bombers						
Tu-95 Bear	100	2	200			
Mya-4 Bison	45	2	90			
Sub total	*145*		*290*			*290*
TOTAL	**2520**		**8825**			**6685**

China: Strategic nuclear weapon delivery systems

Land-based ICBMs/ IRBMs	Number Deployed	Number of Warheads	Warhead Total	Range (km)	Total MT delivery
T-4	4	1×5 MT	4	13,000	20
T-3	10	1×2–3 MT	10	5600	20
T-2	50	1×200 KT-1 MT	50	3200	15
T-1	50	1×20 KT	50	1100	1
Sea-based SLBMs					
CSS-NX-4	12	1×2 MT	12	4000	24
Strategic bombers					
B-6	90	1×1 MT	90		90
TOTAL	**226**		**226**		**170**

Intermediate/Medium Range Nuclear Systems (inc France and UK) end 1983

Missile/Aircraft designation	Year first deployed	Range (km)	CEP (m)	Warhead(s)	Inventory	Programme status
USSR						
SS-4 Sandal	1959	1800	2400	1×MT	223	Phasing out
SS-5 Skean	1961	3500	1200	1×MT	16	Phasing out
SS-20	1976/77	5000	400	3×150-KT MIRV	360	Total figure, two-thirds Europe range
SS-N-5 Serb	1963	1200	n.a.	1×MT	30	3 each on Golf II SSKs
Tu-16/Tu-22/Tu-22M medium range bombers					815	Includes naval air force
USA						
Pershing II	1983	1800	40	1×40 KT	16	108 launchers by 1985
GLCM	1983	2500	50	1×200 KT	16	464 missiles by 1988
Poseidon/Trident	1971/80					400 Poseidon warheads assigned to SACEUR
SLCM	1983	2400	50	1×200 KT	44	Submarine and surface ship launched. 900+ by 1987
F-111E/F	1967	1900	—	6×B43	156	Aircraft based in UK
UK						
Polaris A-3	1967	4600	800	3×200-KT MRV	64	On 4 SSBNs being replaced by the Chevaline system
Trident II (D-5)	(1990s)	10,000	250	8×355-KT MIRV	—	Replacing Polaris from the 1990s, with 64 launchers on 4 submarines
FRANCE						
SSBS S-3	1980	3000	n.a.	1×1-MT	18	
MSBS M-20	1977	3000	n.a.	1×1-MT	80	On 5 SSBNs
MSBS M-4	(1985)	4000	n.a.	6×150-KT MRV	—	On the 6th SSBN; total programme, 96 (by 1992)
Mirage IVA	1964	1600	n.a.	1×60 KT	33	15 aircraft tactical, 1985

Soviet Union (including WP air forces) fields some 2500 nuclear-capable strike aircraft with combat radii of 400–1600 km. NATO (including France) has some 1000+ nuclear-capable strike aircraft with combat radii of 600–950 km. In addition approximately 75 carrier aircraft could be in range, plus reinforcement from USA.

5
Soviet
Strategic
Forces

The Soviet Union, like the United States, has a triad of strategic nuclear forces, but their structure is not a mirror image of the rival land-based ICBMs, sea-launched missiles and long-range aircraft. It has developed around different geographical, political and strategic imperatives and around a different technological base. This is more reactive than initiative, is reluctant to throw old concepts away, and relies heavily on modifications to half-proved systems.

It is a relatively straightforward matter to assess the future shape of US forces as much as two decades hence—with Soviet forces it is much more difficult. Even during open sessions of talks on arms reduction performance details of Soviet weaponry are released only when there is a diplomatic advantage in doing so. Information about future trends and long-range planning is virtually non-existent and must be based on intelligence assessments.

These assessments often function as the political imperatives behind the modernization of western forces. It has frequently been pointed out, for example, in the MX debates, that the Soviet Union has deployed several generations of new ICBMs since the USAF's mature Minuteman programme was established in the early 1970s. There is another argument, however. The Soviet Union has five different types of ICBM, amounting to approximately the same total as the Minuteman IIs and IIIs. It is important to ask why.

Viktor Suvorov put it like this (*Inside the Soviet Army*, Hamish Hamilton, London, 1982): 'Not one of them is of really good quality. Some lack accuracy and have too low a payload and too low a range, but are kept in service because they are more reliable than other types . . . the fact is that the rocket forces have been developed piecemeal. Soviet industry is unable to turn out long production-runs of rockets quickly. Often a really good rocket can only be produced in small numbers because the US will only sell a small quantity of the parts needed for it. For example, if the Americans only sell 79 precision fuel filters, the Soviets will be unable to produce more than this number of rockets.'

Suvorov goes on to point out the shortage of uranium and plutonium for making thermonuclear triggers. Because one trigger is needed for one thermonuclear weapon, whatever its yield, this has led to the Soviet preoccupation with very large yield warheads, as well as offsetting the doubtful accuracy of the delivery system.

The Soviet triad

The current inventory of Soviet intercontinental delivery systems capable of reaching the United States consists of 1398 ICBM launchers, 950 SLBM launchers and 156 long-range bombers mounting approximately 7000 warheads between them. All of this adds up to more delivery systems than the United States possesses, and greater throw weight, but fewer warheads. This mismatch, as well as the fact that a far

greater number of Soviet warheads are mounted on ICBMs rather than on submarines or manned bombers, is one of the disparities that attempts at strategic arms control are attempting to resolve.

Land-based missiles

The Strategic Rocket Forces, *Raketnyye Voyska Strategischeskovo Naznacheniya* (RVSN), controls all military ICBMs, IRBMs and MRBMs, and its carefully selected personnel are the elite of the Soviet armed forces. It was established as a separate service in Dec. 1959 and its first commander was Chief Marshal of Artillery, M. I. Nedelin. The RVSN's first operational equipment was rudimentary: four regiments armed with the 750-mile range radio-command guided missile, codenamed *Shyster* by NATO, but the technology for huge new launchers was emerging from the space programme. In 1957, a 51-year-old candidate member of the Politburo named Leonid Brezhnev, had been put in charge of the Soviet missile production and space programme. Another key protagonist of missile development in this period was Dimitry Ustinov, then Minister of Defence Industries and now Minister of Defence and Marshal of the Soviet Union. Directly under their tutelage worked the 'chief designer' whose identity was kept highly secret.

The chief designer became a legendary figure. When the United States planned to launch an artificial satellite in early 1958, the Chief Designer did it in Oct. 1957. When the United States announced its intention to put a satellite around the Sun in 1959, the Chief Designer beat them by a month and three weeks before Alan Shephard's planned suborbital flight in the Mercury capsule. On April 12, 1961, Yuri Gagarin became the first man to orbit the earth. The seemingly superhuman Chief Designer, with whose achievements Khrushchev used to taunt the Americans, was Sergei Pavlovich Korolyov, born in 1906, the same year as Brezhnev.

Korolyov made his first rocket test in 1934 and by the late 1930s he was working at the Jet Propulsion Institute. He survived Stalin's purges, in which the director, his deputy and most of the institute's research team were liquidated, and worked while under arrest with Andrei Tupolev, who was himself a detainee, during World War II. Soon after the end of the war he was at Kasputin Yar in Central Asia, working with captured German scientists on developments of the V-2. (The United States was doing the very same thing with different German scientists at White Sands, New Mexico.) With direct Politburo access and massive industrial funding, Korolyov's missile and space programme put the Soviet Union on the map as a true postwar superpower—a direct contender with the United States. Korolyov died of a heart condition in 1966 and only then was it revealed that he was the Chief Designer.

There had been setbacks. On Oct. 24, 1960, Nedelin and the key staff of the RVSN were killed when one of the big new experimental military

An SS-8 ICBM is hauled through Red Square. The type of trailer gives clues to a missile's characteristics. A light trailer implies a liquid-fuelled missile with a non-storable propellant. A heavy trailer, as here, means either solid or storable onboard liquid propellant and hence quick-reaction silo launching. The SS-8s are now deactivated, while a formidable new generation of ICBMs has entered service through the 1970s with Soviet strategic rocket forces.

rockets blew up on its launch pad. Two years later the plan to put intermediate-range missiles into Cuba and thus get some target coverage of the United States developed into an extremely dangerous nuclear crisis. Khrushchev backed down. Soon he was out of power and in disgrace and the Soviet Union embarked on an immense, accelerated programme to develop means of striking the United States with nuclear weapons delivered by rocket. There would be no more Cubas — no more humiliations.

In the first years of the Brezhnev regime, from 1964, the Soviet Union's strategic weapons programme concentrated on increasing the number of land-based launchers, first in order to catch up with, then to overhaul, the United States. As a result, the breakdown of the Soviet 'triad' does not match its US counterpart.

The main developments in the 1970s were concerned not so much with increasing the numbers of ICBM but with replacing the first-generation missiles with second-generation SS-17s, SS-18s and SS-19s. More than half the total number of land-based launchers are now new-generation and equipped with MIRV warheads (multiple independently targeted re-entry vehicles). The US Department of Defense and independent sources broadly agree on the number and breakdown of Soviet ICBMs.

	Number	Year entered service
SS-11	580	1966
SS-13	60	1965
SS-17	150	1975
SS-18	308	1974
SS-19	300	1974

(The designation 'SS' is the US reporting system. The Soviet Union has its own military and industrial designation system.)

SS-11 (NATO — Sego)
The first model SS-11 became operational in 1968. Replacement of part of the force with SS-17s was completed by 1982 and others continue to make way for SS-19s. Two models of this liquid-fuelled 6000-mile + range missile remain operational.
SS-11 Mod 2: It differs from the retired Mod 1 in carrying penaids. It has a single RV of higher yield than the comparable Minuteman II but less accurate.
SS-11 Mod 3: First operational Soviet missile with MRVs (3 × 300 KT). More than 60 have been emplaced.
SS-13 (NATO — Savage)
Only 60 of these three-stage solid-propellant/liquid-propellant missiles are operational. They are hot-launched from silos like Minuteman.
Propulsion: 3-stage, solid propellant.
Guidance: Inertial.
CEP: 2 km.
Warhead: 1 MT.
Length: 20 m.
Range: 8000 km (6200 mi.).

Soviet ICBM/IRBM missile sites

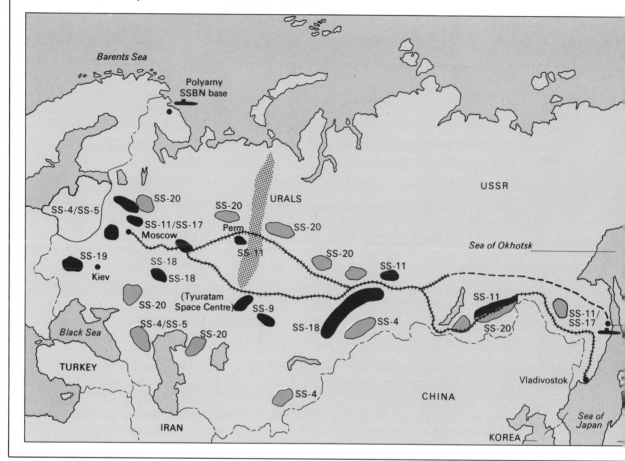

SS-17
This is a two-stage liquid-propellant ICBM, designated RS-16 in the Soviet system. It is deployed in SS-11 silos and is the least accurate of the new-generation missiles. It is believed to be able to deliver four warheads over a range of up to 10,000 km and is cold-launched, that is, it is brought out of its silos on a 'sabot' by a gas generator before the main motors are fired. This minimizes damage to the silo and could allow reloads to be fired. Rapid reloading is precluded by the SALT II treaty, this according to the US definition, being anything under 24 hours.

Two versions are operational:–
SS-17 Mod 1: Four 800-kiloton MIRVs designed for high-speed atmospheric re-entry.
SS-17 Mod 2: Mounts single large five-megaton warhead. Propulsion: two-stage liquid propellant.
CEP: 500 m (0·3 mi.).
Length: 24 m.
Range: (6200 mi.).

SS-18
The huge SS-18 is the missile that has so alarmed US proponents of the 'window of vulnerability' theory. Its power, accuracy and sheer size (twice as big as the MX), plus the fact that it can be cold-launched and thus in theory reloaded, seemed to make it the war-fighting silo smasher that put the Minuteman force in deadly peril.

What has been firmly deduced is that the SS-18 certainly has greater throw-weight than any other US or Soviet ICBM and greater accuracy and flexibility than the SS-9 missile it replaced. It is believed to be capable of delivering eight or ten MIRV warheads over a range of up to 10,000 km. A larger number of warheads can be accommodated at the expense of range. Four versions have been identified.
SS-18 Mod 1: This carries a single large warhead (18-25 megatons) for use against deep underground shelters such as the NORAD headquarters situated beneath Cheyenne Mountain.
SS-18 Mod 2: Main operational version. Carries 8-10 large warheads (2 megatons each) on PBV (post-boost vehicle).
SS-18 Mod 3: This is a long-range single warhead version. A CEP accuracy of 590 ft (180 m) has been recorded in trials.
SS-18 Mod 4: This is a reported new version carrying up to 14 warheads. According to Soviet sources no more than ten have been flown. Therefore the rest can be assumed to be decoys or other penaids, which does not exceed SALT II.
Length: 35 m.
Range: (Mod 1 and 3) 6500 mi.
(Mod 2) 5750 mi.

SS-19
Testing of this light, two-stage liquid propellant missile began in 1974 and it is replacing older SS-11s. It is longer than the SS-11 and the newer SS-17, so it needs considerable modification to the existing silos in which 300 have been emplaced. It carries fewer warheads than the huge SS-18 Mod 2 but the US Department of Defense rates it

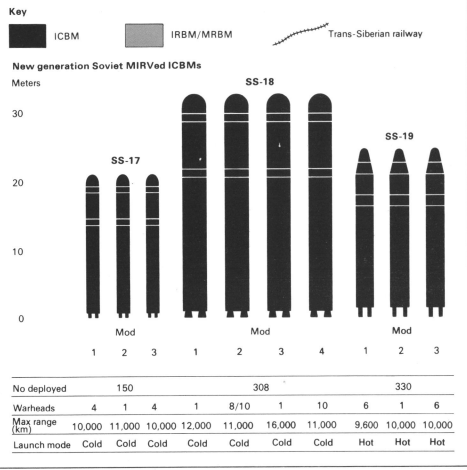

Key

■ ICBM	■ IRBM/MRBM	┈┼┼┼┼┈ Trans-Siberian railway

New generation Soviet MIRVed ICBMs

SS-17   SS-18   SS-19

	Mod 1	Mod 2	Mod 3	Mod 1	Mod 2	Mod 3	Mod 4	Mod 1	Mod 2	Mod 3
No deployed	150			308				330		
Warheads	4	1	4	1	8/10	1	10	6	1	6
Max range (km)	10,000	11,000	10,000	12,000	11,000	16,000	11,000	9,600	10,000	10,000
Launch mode	Cold	Cold	Cold	Cold	Cold	Cold	Cold	Hot	Hot	Hot

as having a capable combination of accuracy and yield.

SS-19 Mod 1 has six 550-kiloton-yield MRVs, and a Mod 2 version with a single large five-megaton-yield warhead has been tested. The SS-19 uses a hot launch, where the missile engine is ignited within the silo.

US sources reported that a new solid-fuelled ICBM was tested from Plesetsk in Oct. 1982. It was assumed to be either a fifth-generation follow-on to the SS-18 and 19 or a mobile booster for the SS-20. This matches reports of a small mobile intercontinental ballistic missile similar in concept to the US 'Midgetman'.

The organization of the Strategic Rocket Forces

The RVSN is both an operational and an administrative organization. It is commanded by General V. F. Tolubko, a tank veteran of World War II, who became Deputy Commander-in-Chief of the rocket forces in 1960 and their commander in 1972. The Commander of the RVSN is a Deputy Minister of Defence and equal in rank to the commanders of the ground forces, the air forces, national air defence and the navy. In peacetime the RVSN reports to the Minister of Defence. In wartime the rocket force would be controlled by the Defence Council through the Supreme Commander. A decision on the use of ICBMs would be made by the Defence Council, that is, the

Politburo, who could bypass RVSN command if necessary.

The RVSN's intercontinental ballistic missile force is deployed in missile complexes strung out generally along the line of the Trans-Siberian railway. It is structured in three rocket armies, three independent rocket corps, ten to twelve rocket divisions, and has large numbers of technical and research establishments at its disposal, with three test-firing ranges. Personnel strength is quoted at 325,000, plus 500,000 civilians.

A rocket army consists of ten divisions, each 7000 to 8000 strong. Its headquarters can use flying command posts based on the Il-18 airframe, although their capabilities compared with the US Strategic Air Command's Looking Glass aircraft are not known. A rocket division is made up of ten regiments, with, in addition, a technical base. Each regiment is made up of between 250 and 400 men, depending on the type of missile deployed. A rocket regiment consists of the commander, his staff, five duty launch teams, a guard company and an emergency repair team.

The regiment controls an ICBM battery group comprising either six or ten silos, while the division controls a main base support area, and a facility for transferring missiles and equipment from rail to road, serviced by the separate technical base unit 3000 to 4000 strong.

Each regiment has an underground command post which is always manned by a duty team of officers with direct communication links to the divisional commander, the rocket army commander, the RVSN commander and the Supreme Command. The regiment also has a mobile command centre, based on motor vehicles, to take control should the fixed centre be threatened.

The independent rocket corps are organized by the rocket armies. However, they have three or four divisions rather than ten, are armed with shorter-range missiles and can be integrated in the tactical operations of other Soviet armed forces. Separate rocket divisions, subordinated directly to the RVSN commander, form the operational reserve.

Ballistic missile submarines
When Soviet forces overran German secret weapon testing sites on the Baltic in 1945, among the half-completed prototypes they captured were containers designed to be towed behind U-boats. They had found the remains of the *Laffarentzprojekt*, a plan to hit the United States with sea-launched missiles. From positions off the US coastline, the containers would have been ballasted to come upright and then, from them, a V-2 could have been launched against New York. They were never used operationally but the implications were clear and the concept was eagerly explored by Soviet scientists in a plan code-named *Golem*.

Development of a submarine-launched ballistic missile proper began in 1953 and, following tests of Scud missiles launched from a modified *Zulu* class submarine in 1955, at least seven Z-class were rebuilt in 1955-6, with two launch tubes running the depth of the keel and conning tower to accommodate a new purpose-designed missile, code-named SS-N-4 Sark by NATO. These were followed by the purpose-designed diesel-powered *Golf* class, armed with three of the missiles, and at least 22 were built up to 1961. Simultaneously, the first of the nuclear-powered *Hotel* class was under construction, similarly carrying three of these cumbersome liquid-fuelled missiles. The range was about 600 km (373 mi.) and these short-ranged SLBMs, half of them mounted on diesel-powered submarines, accounted for much of Soviet sea-launched strategic potential as late as 1970.

Since then some 60 modern nuclear-powered ballistic-missile submarines have joined the fleet. The total now is 83 submarines mounting 989 missiles. The most modern missiles have multiple warheads and sufficient range to operate from Soviet home waters, putting them, to all intents and purposes, beyond the reach of US antisubmarine warfare. The *Hotel* class of the early 1960s was followed by the *Yankee* class, with 12 to 16 launch tubes and with SS-N-6 Sawfly missiles, which had a range of 3000 to 4000 km. The most modern *Delta*-class submarines carry 12 to 16 SS-N-8 missiles, which have a range of 8000 to 9000 mi. The *Delta* III carries 16 SS-N-18 liquid-propellant missiles, which have two stages and a triple MIRV warhead. In 1979 a new missile, code-named the SS-NX-20, was tested. It is believed to carry 12 MIRVs and to have a range of 8300 km. This is the missile assumed to arm the huge new submarine of the *Typhoon* class (also code-named *Sierra*), first launched in Sept. 1980. Propelled by two nuclear reactors, the *Typhoon* is 170 m long (the length of two and a half Boeing 747s) and displaces 33,000 tons dived. The *Typhoon* class would operate as a mobile underwater missile silo complex, screened from efforts at antisubmarine warfare by friendly surface forces or by polar ice, its huge size giving it the stability to launch several missiles simultaneously.

The number of disposable warheads at sea is still far less than that of the United States (1309 to 5210) and only 23% of the total number of Soviet warheads. Owing to problems of serviceability and geography the Soviet Union can only deploy 20% of its SSBN force at any one time compared to the US Navy's figure of 50%. Further, it is judged that Soviet ballistic missile submarines are inferior to their US equivalents in most crucial technical respects—they are much noisier and thus much more tactically vulnerable. Moreover, their command control and communications net is more primitive. In spring 1983 it was reported that during exercises the naval command staff were able to communicate for the first time with submerged SSBNs—a technique the US Navy had long since successfully practised.

A particular US fear, however, is of a close-in first strike made without warning. From stations near the coast of the United States or in the Caribbean, submarine-launched missiles could obliterate SAC bomber bases within seven minutes of breaking surface, although technical difficulties in flying depressed trajectories would impose a minimum range of 300 nautical miles. However, flight times to SAC's nearest bomber and tanker bases would be three times as great for missiles fired from the Barents Sea, where most patrols are stationed. Like the US Navy, the Soviet Navy is reported to have developed a cruise missile, designated SS-NX-21, which can be fired from submarine torpedo tubes. This could have the effect of giving the entire submarine fleet a nuclear land attack strategic capability. The Soviet ballistic submarine fleets are based on two major complexes, Polyarny on the Kola peninsula, and at Petropavlovsk-Kamchatsky on the Pacific.

Long-range aviation
The Soviet Union never developed a long-range manned bomber force during World War II—it found another way of reaching Berlin. In the late 1940s the Tupolev design bureau produced a virtual copy of the B-29, the Tu-4 (called Bull by NATO), and this was

The Soviet Navy's first SLBM was the SS-N-4 *Sark*. It was cumbersome, short-ranged and liquid-fuelled, but it pioneered the concept before the US Navy's solid-fuelled Polaris got to sea. Initial tests were carried out with Scud land-based missiles, shown here with Soviet Navy officers. In spite of being first with submarine-launched ballistic missiles, the Soviet Navy has far fewer disposable warheads at sea than the United States.

the very first Soviet strategic weapon delivery system. Of the two domestic products of the early 1950s the turboprop-powered Tupolev Tu-95 Bear and the jet-powered Myasichev M-4 Bison, the pure-jet bomber proved a comparative failure, while the old Bear seems to soldier on and on. There are 45 Bisons designed to carry free-fall bombs and 35 have been adapted as tankers. There are 105 Bear bombers still in service, 70 of them capable of carrying the AS-3 Kangaroo 650-km range air-to-surface missile.

In 1980 Long-Range Aviation (Dal'nyaya Aviat-siya or DA) disposed of 310 intermediate-range Tu-16s, and 535 medium-range bombers, comprising 310 aging Tu-16 Badgers and 125 Tu-22

Blinders, operational since the early 1960s, plus 100 of the much more modern Tu-22M or Backfire, operational since the mid-1970s. Since then Soviet military aviation has undergone a major reorganization. The DA has been relegated to the position of a numbered Air Army (the 36th), with two divisions of Bisons and Badgers. The 46th Air Army, with headquarters at Smolensk, now operates Badgers, Blinders and Backfires in a strike-role in the European theatre.

A major stumbling block during the original SALT talks was the problem of whether or not the DA was targeted against the continental United States, although the Soviet Union argued that the bomber

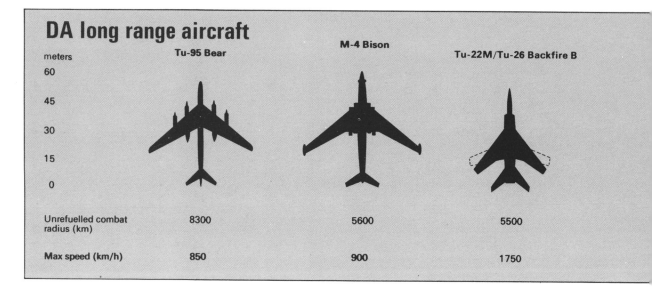

DA long range aircraft

meters	Tu-95 Bear	M-4 Bison	Tu-22M/Tu-26 Backfire B
Unrefuelled combat radius (km)	8300	5600	5500
Max speed (km/h)	850	900	1750

force was not exclusively an intercontinental offensive delivery system. The Backfire's capabilities and its ability to reach the United States with mid-air refuelling became a hotly contested issue. The unratified treaty eventually contained an exchange of statements to the effect that the Backfire was not to be regarded as a heavy bomber unless it was armed with long-range cruise missiles. Meanwhile, the numbers of Backfires in service both with the DA and with Naval Aviation are increasing significantly. Some will be new aircraft, Backfire-Bs, with an estimated production rate of 42 a year, while others will be older A models, rebuilt to -B standard. A new re-engined variant (called Backfire-C by NATO) began to enter service in 1983. The Soviet Navy currently operates 80 Tu-22Ms, armed with AS-4 Kingfish air-to-surface missiles, together with more than 300 old Badger and Blinder medium-range bombers.

The Soviet medium-bomber force of both the DA and the Navy, with its capabilities now far extended by the Tu-22M/AS-4 combination, has always been a particular concern of UK air-defence planners. This has been grown into a general concern about the vulnerability of the NATO Atlantic sea route to attack from both below and above the water.

Although the Soviet Union virtually abandoned heavy bomber development in the 1950s, it did not cease entirely. Production of the very useful long-range Bears still continues at a trickle to replace those lost or worn out.

Throughout the 1970s there were persistent reports of a Soviet bomber that was bigger and more capable than even Backfire. It was known as Bomber-X in the West, then Ram-P, after a satellite photograph revealed a big variable-geometry aircraft on the apron at the Ramenskoye flight test centre. In 1982 it was given the US Department of Defense's reporting name, Blackjack. The bomber comes from the Tupolev design bureau and, according to US

reports, is 25% bigger than the B-1. It does, however, show overall similarities in design, and is meant to be faster, although it has slightly less range than its US counterpart. The Department of Defense report goes on to claim that Blackjack would be the carrier for a new air-launched cruise missile under development.

Strategic air defence
Since 1948 Soviet air defence has been grouped as a separate command, the Voiska Provivovozdushnoy Oborony Strany (or PVO Strany). Very large numbers of launchers, interceptor aircraft and radar sites are still deployed, despite the long decline in US manned-bomber strength. Efforts to develop antiballistic missile defences and satellite killers have also been strenuous, with PKO (anti-space defence) and PRO (anti-rocket defence) established as separate sub-organizations in the mid-1960s. PVO Strany has 630,000 troops, organized into ten air-defence districts, with special emphasis on Moscow and the oil-producing centre of Baku, numerous air-defence regiments and some 14 specialist schools.

The commander of PVO-Strany since 1978 is Marshal of Aviation Aleksandr Ivanovich Koldunov, a fighter ace of World War II, with 46 enemy aircraft to his credit. He commands the three basic components of the force—manned interceptor squadrons, radio technical troops and zenith rocket troops—and close ties are maintained between PVO units and civil defence troops.

The Radiotekhnicheskiye Voiska TRV, or radio technical troops, are responsible for the electronic surveillance of airspace, operating space systems and a dense and overlapping network of more than 6000 radars. There has been a programme of launches, putting two Cosmos satellites into highly elliptical semi-synchronous orbits at any one time, which would give a launch-detection capability over US ICBM fields. There are three, and possibly a fourth,

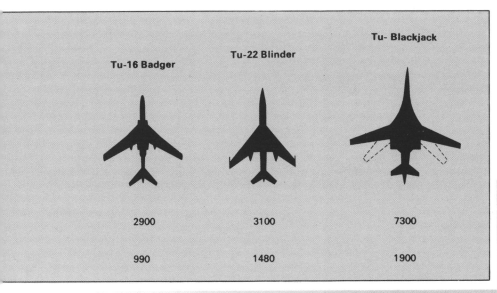

Tu-16 Badger   **Tu-22 Blinder**   **Tu- Blackjack**

| 2900 | 3100 | 7300 |
| 990 | 1480 | 1900 |

Below: The Myasichev Mya-4 *Bison*, the Soviet equivalent of the B-52. Unlike the US aircraft, the Soviet Union's first pure jet strategic bomber was not a success in service and was built only in small numbers. Some 43 continue as bomber/ reconnaissance aircraft and 30 more have been rebuilt as tankers.

over the horizon-backscatter (OTH-B, *see* page 78) long-range radars sited near Minsk, near Nikolayev in the Caucasus, and in the Far East looking north towards routes of entry over the North Pole.

The Soviet Union possesses the only operational·antiballistic missile system in the world. The ABM Treaty of 1972 permitted a total of 100 ABM launchers to each side, based on two sites, to protect the national capital, and an ICBM site. In 1974 a protocol altered this to one site only. The United States built a system to protect a Minuteman complex in North Dakota, but it was only operational perhaps for a day (if at all). The Soviet Union, meanwhile, continued with the activation of an ABM defence of the national capital, completing a process that had been underway since the mid-1960s.

The Galosh missile first appeared in public in 1964, or rather, concealed in a container as it was trundled through Red Square. There have been only scant glimpses of it since. To be able to intercept an incoming missile it must be capable of enormous acceleration, with three propulsion stages and a large nuclear yield (as much as three megatons), knocking out incoming warheads by sheer brute power. The prospect of huge nuclear explosion detonating above US cities in their 'defence' was a strong motive for the United States to abandon ABM development in the 1970s.

The original 64 Galosh launchers were reduced by half in 1979-80, perhaps as a recognition of the system's obsolescence in the face of MIRVs or, according to the US Department of Defense, to make way for the deployment of a new system. The Soviet Union is believed to have at least two antiballistic missile defence projects under development. One, code-named ABM-X-2, remains very shadowy. ABM-X-3 is reported by the Department of Defense to be a rapidly deployable system, incorporating a new

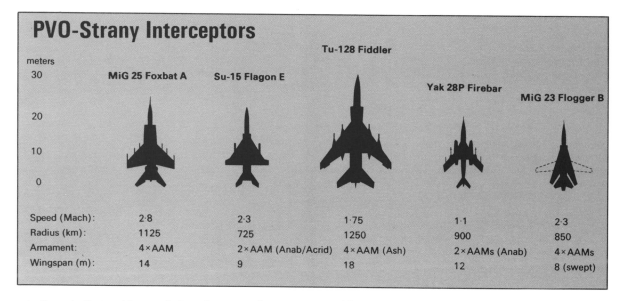

PVO-Strany Interceptors

	MiG 25 Foxbat A	Su-15 Flagon E	Tu-128 Fiddler	Yak 28P Firebar	MiG 23 Flogger B
Speed (Mach):	2·8	2·3	1·75	1·1	2·3
Radius (km):	1125	725	1250	900	850
Armament:	4×AAM	2×AAM (Anab/Acrid)	4×AAM (Ash)	2×AAMs (Anab)	4×AAMs
Wingspan (m):	14	9	18	12	8 (swept)

missile, missile-tracking and phased array radar.

As it stands now, the ABM defence of Moscow begins with five large radars of the Hen-series, widely dispersed throughout the USSR, with known sites at Irkutsk, in Latvia and near the Barents Sea. A large, phased array radar system based on ten sites, with a range of 2000 km, is being built to supplement this system.

Warning from the Hen-series radars (Department of Defense code-names are used) is passed on to the four Galosh complexes ringing Moscow. Each complex consists of two separate radar groups and eight launchers. Each group comprises of one 'Dog House' or 'Cat House' radar, which have a range of around 3000 km, and two Try Add engagement radars. A new system to replace the Dog House radars, which date back to the 1960s, is reported to be under construction.

In mid-1983 it was reported that a new missile had been deployed in East Germany. Designated SA-12, it is stated by US intelligence that its primary function is as an ABM defence against the Pershing II.

Antiaircraft defence

The German Luftwaffe never developed a practical long-range strategic bombing aircraft during World War II. The advocate of a 'Ural bomber' programme, Luftwaffe General Wever, was killed in a plane crash in 1938 and his plans died with him. Moscow and Soviet industrial centres never came under sustained strategic air attack by the Germans, but when Soviet troops overran Berlin and Dresden in 1945, they saw just how devastating the long reach of RAF Bomber Command and the USAAF Eighth Air Force had been. The lesson was not lost and strategic air defence became a key postwar military priority for the Soviet Union. PVO-Strany was separated from the ground forces in 1948, MiG 15 jets were operational by 1949 and SA-1 SAMs were deployed in two huge concentric rings around Moscow by 1955. The much more capable SA-2 was deployed from 1962 onwards.

Today PVO-Strany deploys approximately 12,400 missile launchers at about 1400 fixed sites and 2250 interceptor aircraft, plus at least ten Moss AWACS warning and control aircraft. A new AWACS, based on the Il-76 airframe, code-named *Mainstay*, is entering service. Airborne early warning, new interceptors and new missiles are part of the efforts to close the low-level gap. The first Soviet weapon identified as having a degree of anti-cruise missile capacity is the new SA-10, with a maximum speed of Mach 6 and a range of 50 km. The system uses a tower-mounted surveillance radar to pick up low-flying targets. At present transportable SA-10 batteries are deployed in small numbers to protect high-value critical targets within the Soviet Union.

The air forces of the other Warsaw Pact countries have, in addition, interceptor regiments and SAM sites mounting SA-2s and SA-3s. In early 1983 the construction was completed of a chain of SAM complexes mounting the 290-km range SA-5 missile, which stretched the length of the European central front from the Baltic coast of East Germany to southern Czechoslovakia.

From August 1978 onwards PVO Strany appears to have been merged progressively with Army Air Defence, the Voiska Protivovizdushnoi Obornoy Sukhoputiniykh Voisk (PVO SV), which provides tactical SAM defence of ground forces, using a wide range of short-range guns and missiles and specialized tactical vehicles. By 1983 most of the PVO-Strany's air defence district headquarters were disbanded and their functions taken over by the Military District headquarters. Currently only five PVO Strany District headquarters remain—at Archangel, Kiev, Moscow, Sverdlovsk and Novossibirsk. The operational implications of this change are not yet clear but the tragic shooting down of a Korean Boeing 747 airliner took place while it was going on, with the decision to shoot being taken at Military District HQ.

Manned interceptors
In the 1960s the air threat to the Soviet Union came from high-level bombers. The threat today comes from low-level penetrators and cruise missiles. Aircraft such as the Mach 3 MiG 25 Foxbat represent the response to the first threat, designed to get to high altitude as fast as possible and launch air-to-air missiles at long range. The bigger, slower Tupolev Tu-128 and Sukhoi Su-15 were designed to do the same thing at longer range. Numerically the most important PVO-Strany interceptor is the MiG-23 Flogger B/G variable-geometry multi-role fighter. The Flogger B, with its 'High Lark' radar, was described in the US fiscal year 1979 Posture Statement as the first Soviet aircraft with a demonstrated, if rudimentary, ability to track and engage targets flying below its own altitude.

This 'look-down' ability of a modern radar to distinguish moving targets seen from above against the background clutter of the ground itself is a vital prerequisite of defence against fast low-flying aircraft and cruise missiles. The second component is a 'shoot down' missile that can itself seek out its target from above.

The Soviets are beginning to deploy aircraft with 'look down-shoot down' capability, notably the MiG 25 Foxhound (a two-seat Foxbat equipped with a highly capable radar) mounting an AA-9 air-to-air missile.

In 1979 US sources reported a new fighter aircraft under development by the Mikoyan-Gurevich design bureau. It was designated Ram-L (Ramenskoye Type L) and later MiG-29 Fulcrum. The MiG-29 is a multi-role air-superiority aircraft but could function very efficiently in the interceptor role with the appropriate radar and new-generation look-down shoot-down missiles.

Civil defence
An ordered, militarized society like the Soviet Union finds little difficulty in marshalling the willpower and the resources of its citizens for civil defence purposes. A civil defence organization was established as early as 1932 and in 1961 responsibility was transferred from the Ministry of the Interior to the Ministry of Defence, making civil defence a branch of the Army. The 50,000 regular troops, with an officer school at Balashika, are combined with 65,000 reserves and are commanded by a Deputy Minister of Defence, General A. T. Altunin, who was appointed with a wide-ranging brief and lavish funding in 1972 to reinvigorate the organization after the antiballistic missile effort was scaled down. Military civil defence staffs exist at each level of the Soviet government structure, with local civilian staffs in towns and factories. Civil defence staff also run courses for part-time volunteers, with numbers estimated at up to 15

million. Information reaches the bulk of the population by means of lectures, broadcasts and leaflets.

The Soviet population, although concentrated in a triangle bounded by Leningrad, Odessa and Kuznetsk containing the core areas of Moscow, Donets, Baku and the Urals, is not as compressed into urban centres as is that of the United States. The 1000 largest cities contain less than half the population; only 18 exceed 1 million in population and Moscow has 7 million.

Current civil defence doctrine reportedly entails clearing the cities while essential services are manned on a shift basis. Those operating these services will have recourse to blast and fallout shelters in factories. The remainder of the urban population will be evacuated to rural areas and will construct shelters if none exist. Soviet authorities claim that this would take between two and five days. There is also training and practice to protect the economic assets, on which the survival of the evacuated populations and any postwar 'recovery' depend. The US Boeing company tested the directions in the Soviet civil defence manual on protecting machine tools. They covered several kinds with sandbags and exploded 500 tons of TNT close enough to get a pulse of overpressure simulating a nuclear explosion. At 1300 psi, heavy machinery bedded on Styrofoam and with its critical parts packed with earth and metal turnings, remained operable.

The Soviet government machine has of course ensured its own survival. There are deep, very hard urban shelters, a system of evacuation for key commanders, a secure communications net and some 75 command posts within 120 km of Moscow with accommodation for at least 11,000 officials. There are reports of an alternative government underground command centre near Kuybishev 850 km southeast of Moscow.

In 1978 there was another 'gap' scare in the United States, very like the bomber and missile gaps that went before. It was a response to claims that in an all-out strategic exchange, Soviet fatalities would be 4-5% of the population and the US ones 50%. No matter how crushing or effective an attack, effective civil defence would protect key economic assets, allow a rapid recovery from the war much as devastated Germany and Japan recovered, and thus produce a 'winner' and a 'loser'.

US strategists, think-tank experts and intelligence agencies became very interested in the subject of Soviet civil defence but they produced contradictory conclusions. The Department of Defense reported that, although the city evacuation plan looked impressive, they doubted its effectiveness in practice and speculated how the huge displaced populations would survive, with the economic structure in ruins. It further doubted the existence of a comprehensive programme for hardening Soviet economic installations. Other, more hawkish observers came to the conclusion that 'Soviet preparations substantially undermine the concept of deterrence that forms the cornerstone of US security.'

6
The
Nuclear
Battle
for
Europe

Since 1945, when US and Soviet troops met on the Elbe in the ruins of Hitler's Reich, the political geography of Europe has been fixed. The Soviet Union has used military force to keep its satellites in line in East Germany, Hungary, Czechoslovakia and, by proxy, in Poland. The Western European powers have used military force in the drawn-out process of colonial retreat from Algeria to the Falklands. There has been no shooting war between European sovereign powers for almost 40 years except marginally during the Turkish invasion of Cyprus in 1974. And yet Europe remains a continent in arms sitting on a destructive arsenal, the power of which Kaisers and dictators could never have dreamed. A very large part of that arsenal is directly controlled by the United States.

Following the Berlin crisis of 1948, those nations of Europe liberated from German occupation by Anglo-American military power signed a treaty of mutual assistance. In April 1949 the final security treaty was signed by the United States, Canada, the United Kingdom, France, the Netherlands, Belgium, Luxembourg, Portugal, Iceland, Denmark and Norway to establish the North Atlantic Treaty Organization or NATO. Greece and Turkey joined in 1951, West Germany in 1954 and Spain in 1982.

In 1955, nominally as a response to West Germany's rearmament within NATO, a coalition of countries liberated in 1944-5 by Soviet military power signed the Warsaw Pact mutual defence treaty —Poland, Czechoslovakia, Hungary, Romania, Bulgaria, East Germany and Albania, plus the Soviet Union itself.

There has been dissension in both camps. France withdrew from NATO's military command in 1966 and Albania broke with the Warsaw Pact in 1968. Greece withdrew from the NATO military command in 1974 and rejoined in 1981. A marshal of the Soviet Union has always been commander-in-chief of the Warsaw Pact forces, just as a US general and admiral have always been NATO's supreme commanders, on land and sea—SACEUR and SACLANT respectively.

NATO has always been a nuclear-armed alliance. The first nuclear presence was 32 B-29 bombers of US Strategic Air Command, which came to Britain in the summer of 1949. Because NATO's conventional force levels, in terms of manpower and equipment on the ground, were at an early date fixed on a scale far less than that of the Soviet Union's huge army, nuclear weapons have always been NATO's 'deterrent' against a conventional attack. There have been several important shifts of doctrine, from massive retaliation, via tripwire to flexible response (*see* page 000), but the first use of nuclear weapons in reply to an overwhelming conventional attack remains NATO policy today.

Going nuclear
Nuclear weapons in Europe on both sides fall into three broad categories: first, short-range—missiles up to a range of 200 km, artillery, nuclear air defence system, mines and ground attack aircraft; secondly, medium-range—missiles with a range up to 100 km designed to operate at army or Soviet front level, and interdiction aircraft; and, thirdly, long-range—missiles and aircraft with a range greater than 1000 km (LRTNF or long-range tactical nuclear force, sometimes referred to as 'Eurostrategic').

Small nuclear devices were developed from the comparatively large and cumbersome atomic weapons of 1945 in a remarkably short time. They were deployed very widely in Europe by NATO from the mid-1950s onwards, when they seemed to provide defence 'on the cheap' in the face of Soviet conventional superiority. They ranged from atomic demolition munitions (ADMs or nuclear mines), placed to block Turkish mountain passes or German Autobahn junctions, to such fearsome devices as the Davy Crockett jeep-mounted missiles with a blast radius greater than its range. Some of these relatively crude devices have been withdrawn but more than 6000 battlefield nuclear weapons remain, ranging from eight-inch howitzers, via Lance missiles with a range of 110 km, to Nike-Hercules area anti-aircraft missiles with nuclear warheads. The Soviet Union has a similar line-up of nuclear-capable artillery, short- and medium-range missiles and aircraft. Its forces even deploy some nuclear-capable mortars.

The dual key
Soviet nuclear weapons remain in Soviet custody. Of the US battlefield nuclear weapons in Europe, one-third are for the use of US forces, the others are assigned to other NATO countries under 'dual key' control. In this case the warheads are under US control while, the aircraft, missile or howitzer which fires them is under 'host nation' control, and the United States has bilateral agreements for such arrangements with Greece, Italy, the United Kingdom, West Germany and the Netherlands.

The British Royal Artillery in Germany, for example, operates dual-capacity howitzers, capable of firing US nuclear shells, plus a battery of 12 Lance missile-launchers with perhaps some 60 missiles. Each is on a one-British, one-US officer dual key—in effect, a system of electronic and mechanical interlocks forming the 'permissive action link', to prevent unauthorized arming by an 'aberrant or demented individual' to quote the official document. These weapons, whether in US or host nation service, can be fired only with an order from the US national command authority—but how would this work in practice?

In Wintex '83 for example, representative NATO manoeuvres envisaging war on the central front, NATO released tactical nuclear weapons within six days of the first Warsaw Pact incursions. Because the step of employing the first nuclear weapon is so fundamental, a complex structure of command and control must be built and consultative procedures

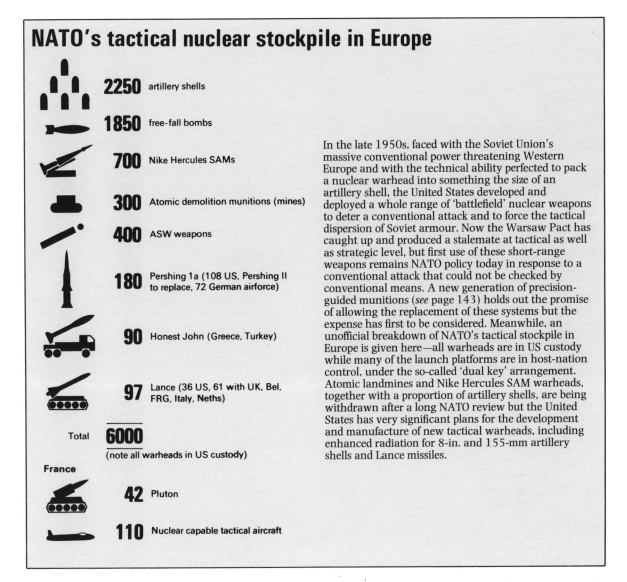

NATO's tactical nuclear stockpile in Europe

2250 artillery shells

1850 free-fall bombs

700 Nike Hercules SAMs

300 Atomic demolition munitions (mines)

400 ASW weapons

180 Pershing 1a (108 US, Pershing II to replace, 72 German airforce)

90 Honest John (Greece, Turkey)

97 Lance (36 US, 61 with UK, Bel, FRG, Italy, Neths)

Total **6000**
(note all warheads in US custody)

France

42 Pluton

110 Nuclear capable tactical aircraft

In the late 1950s, faced with the Soviet Union's massive conventional power threatening Western Europe and with the technical ability perfected to pack a nuclear warhead into something the size of an artillery shell, the United States developed and deployed a whole range of 'battlefield' nuclear weapons to deter a conventional attack and to force the tactical dispersion of Soviet armour. Now the Warsaw Pact has caught up and produced a stalemate at tactical as well as strategic level, but first use of these short-range weapons remains NATO policy today in response to a conventional attack that could not be checked by conventional means. A new generation of precision-guided munitions (*see* page 143) holds out the promise of allowing the replacement of these systems but the expense has first to be considered. Meanwhile, an unofficial breakdown of NATO's tactical stockpile in Europe is given here—all warheads are in US custody while many of the launch platforms are in host-nation control, under the so-called 'dual key' arrangement. Atomic landmines and Nike Hercules SAM warheads, together with a proportion of artillery shells, are being withdrawn after a long NATO review but the United States has very significant plans for the development and manufacture of new tactical warheads, including enhanced radiation for 8-in. and 155-mm artillery shells and Lance missiles.

with 'host nations' brought in. Yet they are deployed close to the front line in response to perceived military needs and commanded by men looking for military solutions. Here is the crux of the problem.

The nuclear threshold

In virtually all NATO gameplans and scenarios the first nuclear weapons to be detonated are tactical, that is, used on the battlefield. In theory the governments of the 15 states of the alliance should be consulted, but in practice matters would turn out differently. If, for example, a US divisional head-quarters in central Germany came under a massive Soviet combined arms conventional attack and was unable to hold the line a request might come to use nuclear artillery to stop the tanks before the guns and their storage dumps were overrun. The request would go up the chain of command, to corps, to CENTAG (Central Army Group), to AFCENT (Allied Forces

Central Europe), to SHAPE and to SACEUR, the Supreme Allied Commander Europe who is also commander of US Europe Command (EUCOM). By that time he would be out of Germany and at SHAPE headquarters in Belgium or an alternative command centre in the United Kingdom. From SACEUR the request would go to the US National Command Authority, where the President would take the decision while trying to consult the German Chancellor. The whole operation would take 24 hours, communications would be deteriorating and the tactical moment would have long since passed.

This could be considered defensive use. The next step would be to use longer-range nuclear weapons to strike 'deep' targets, such as the main operating bases of Warsaw Pact aircraft, either in response to Soviet action or under critical military pressure. This puts NATO on the offensive.

There is a nuclear planning staff at SHAPE which

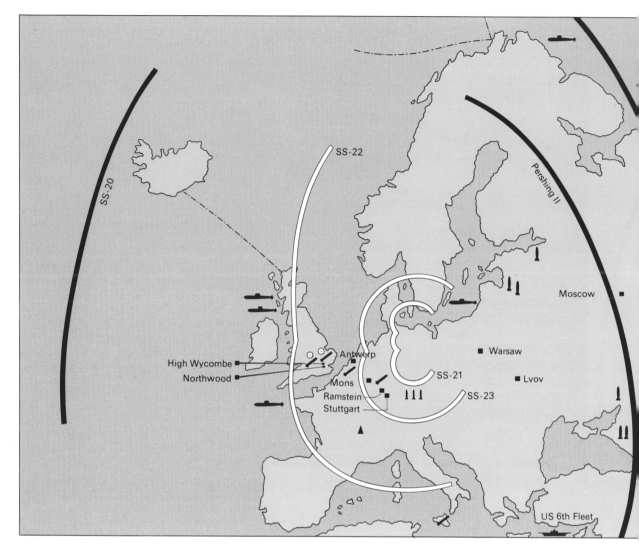

bases its planning on the NATO Document MC 14/3 — the so-called Athens guidelines of 1967, since amended by the nuclear planning group guidelines of 1969, the first-strike guidelines of 1972 and the biannual ministerial guidelines.

MC 14/3 differentiates between three kinds of nuclear response — direct retaliation, deliberate escalation and general nuclear response. SHAPE prepares its own list of critical theatre targets with Pershing Ia and nuclear-capable aircraft at its disposal, plus 400 Poseidon submarine-launched missile warheads to be joined or replaced by GLCMs and Pershing IIs. Part of this force is on quick reaction alert (or QRA) for operational use during or immediately after an attack. As far as operational planning is concerned the SACEUR's Nuclear Operations Plan (NOP) and the US strategic plan (the SIOP) are integrated in several ways, with special 'limited nuclear options' using intercontinental weapons, intended for strikes on Soviet medium-range weapons and other theatre targets.

The request to fire a ground-launched cruise missile from Great Britain aimed at a target deep in Poland, for example, would come from SACEUR level. Dispersed from their main operating bases, a flight of GLCMs would have taken up position on a pre-surveyed site in southern England, ringed by heavily armed troops. In the mobile Launch Control Centre (LCC) two officers face computer keyboards. The LCC is in radio contact via the AFSTACOM satellite network with US European Command, which can send pre-recorded emergency action messages to the LCC, using a radio link code-named Flaming Arrow. EUCOM communicates with the NCA in the United States, and the airborne command posts that would carry the US president and military commanders in wartime can also communicate directly on a range of radio frequencies with each cruise missile convoy. Further back-up and 'redundancy' are provided by USAF Europe's own communication system and NATO's high frequency radio links (code-named 'Cemetery') with the mobile launch-control centres

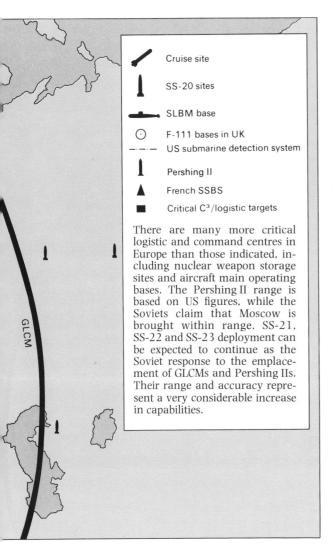

Cruise site

SS-20 sites

SLBM base

⊙ F-111 bases in UK

–·–·– US submarine detection system

Pershing II

▲ French SSBS

■ Critical C³/logistic targets

There are many more critical logistic and command centres in Europe than those indicated, including nuclear weapon storage sites and aircraft main operating bases. The Pershing II range is based on US figures, while the Soviets claim that Moscow is brought within range. SS-21, SS-22 and SS-23 deployment can be expected to continue as the Soviet response to the emplacement of GLCMs and Pershing IIs. Their range and accuracy represent a very considerable increase in capabilities.

GLCM

sophisticated electronics able to stop a massed tank formation with missiles launched from a single aircraft. Stopping tanks was the original reasoning behind enhanced radiation weapons, the so-called 'neutron bomb', which would destroy an armoured attack by making the crew the target, not the tanks themselves. ER weapons, which can be delivered by artillery shells or battlefield-range missiles, are atomic explosives designed to minimize the blast but 'enhance' the deadly radiation effects. They may make military sense, but in no way can they be said to lower the nuclear threshold.

Published Soviet doctrine envisages a war on Europe's central sector brought about by NATO's 'adventurism'. A massive land and air counter-offensive rolls back this aggression and penetrates deep into enemy territory, destroying enemy forces in the process. Speed in overrunning or destroying enemy tactical nuclear weapons is crucial, and the rapid penetration of enemy forces and blurring of the battlefield edge will restrict enemy nuclear options. Should the enemy resort to a tactical nuclear defence, either localized or theatre-wide, then any restraints on the use of theatre nuclear weapons are removed. They become the main and legitimate means of destroying the enemy in battle—indeed hesitation would throw away the advantage of initiative.

This implies pre-emptive attacks on counterforce targets, not just a single salvo but a sustained barrage until all targetable objectives are destroyed. SS-20 missiles based in western Russia can blanket NATO's rearmost launch platform for theatre nuclear forces and pinch out the point of entry for US reinforcements —the United Kingdom. Deterrence has signally failed for Western Europe in this gameplan but the United States is still intact. Would the United States now use its intercontinental arsenal against the Soviet Union or would the use of US theatre weapons against Soviet targets have already set the ICBMs flying?

There is an important difference between the forces of the Warsaw Pact and NATO, brought about not by politics but by geography. The military assets of the pact are closely grouped round, standardized with, and dominated by, the Soviet Union. The resources of NATO are widely dispersed and non-standardized, while the dominant military power is separated by the Atlantic Ocean. Such a power base is vulnerable to severance at both ends, either by European intransigence or US isolationism. NATO calls this the 'decoupling' issue and the most symbolic counter to it is the basing of US ground forces in Europe itself, as much a hostage to US public opinion and political willpower as a rational military deployment.

The second counter to decoupling is the basing of US 'theatre nuclear forces' in Europe. The process originally began because forward basing was the only way of striking the Soviet Union. When US ICBMs and submarine-launched missiles became operational in the early 1960s, US nuclear weapons which were actually based on the ground in Europe became

and main operating bases for cruise missiles. These, however, are not under dual-nation key control. The two USAF officers simply have to type in their six-letter codes and the missile is launched. The only obligation to the 'host nation' is a vaguely worded 30-year-old communiqué that the use of nuclear weapons based in Britain would be a matter for joint decision. It is to be presumed that, by the time a cruise missile was launched, the electronic net that links allied supreme commanders would be severely damaged and the time for diplomatic niceties over.

It will be seen that, in spite of NATO's first-use policy, the employment of tactical nuclear weapons would be sanctioned only when a conventional attack proved overwhelming. Crossing the nuclear threshold depends, therefore, on NATO's ability to resist a conventional attack with a conventional defence. To raise the threshold great hope is held out for the new technology of precision-guided munitions (PGMs) to do just this. A USAF project called 'Assault Breaker' foresees an airborne system guided by

Nuclear-capable artillery

'Atomic artillery' was successfully engineered in the late 1950s and today the large numbers of small short-range artillery-fired atomic projectiles dating from that period swell the headcount of NATO's nuclear weapons in Europe. A sizeable quantity is also stockpiled by the US Army in South Korea. Recent development work has concentrated on increasing the effective ranges of all tube artillery including the nuclear-capable 155 mm and 8 in. (203 mm). The M422 8-in. nuclear shell carries the W33 warhead, using enriched Uranium 235 in oralloy form as its fissile material and has a yield of up to 2 kilotons. It can be fired by the M115 towed howitzer and the M55, M110 and M110A1/A2 self-propelled howitzers at ranges up to 25 km. This round will be supplanted by the XM753, carrying the W-79 enhanced radiation warhead. This is due to be manufactured but will be stockpiled only in the continental United States.

Congress has been less forthcoming with production funds for new 155 mm ammunition to replace and supplant the 3000-plus rounds available for use with the M114 and M198 towed howitzers and M44 and M109 self-propelled guns. There have been grave problems with the XM785 nuclear projectile, carrying the W82 warhead and using plutonium 239 as fissile material. Two yields are planned, one sub-kiloton, the other 4 to 5 kilotons.

The British Army operates over 100 M109 155-mm SP howitzers and 16 8-in. M110 SP howitzers, capable of operating US atomic projectiles under dual-key control.

Neutron Warheads

Artillery shells and battlefield tactical missiles such as Lance are the planned delivery systems for 'neutron' or, more properly, 'enhanced radiation' weapons. Neutron shells have been developed as anti-armour weapons, airburst over a formation on the move, but the crew rather than the vehicles themselves are the target. Because the destructive radius of the blast and heat of a low-yield nuclear weapon is less than that of its flesh and blood killing prompt radiation, ER weapons are advanced as a legitimate military means of stopping armour while avoiding massive collateral damage. The old fission warhead of the Lance, for example, had a 10-kiloton warhead, considered the optimum for forcing the dispersal of Soviet tanks. The ER version would have the same effect, it is argued, but with a 1-kiloton yield. The 203-mm artillery shell would similarly be reduced in yield from 1-2 kilotons to 0·7 kilotons. Lance and 203-mm ER warheads are in production, but will be stockpiled only in the United States—although they only make tactical sense if forward-based in Europe. Their deterrent advantages over conventional or even existing tactical nuclear systems are, however, highly questionable.

Above: M110 self-propelled howitzer of the Royal Artillery.
Left: M109 SP howitzer. Both weapons are capable of firing
US Artillery-Fired Atomic Projectiles (AFAPs), the weapons
themselves being kept in US custody. Enhanced radiation
shells are under development.

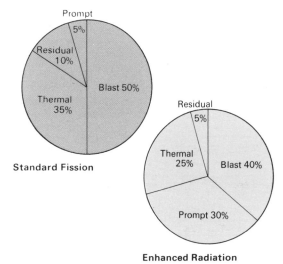

Standard Fission

Prompt
5%
Residual
10%
Blast 50%
Thermal
35%

Enhanced Radiation

Residual
5%
Thermal
25%
Blast 40%
Prompt 30%

Collateral effects of normal fission and enhanced radiation
weapons. A one-kiloton enhanced radiation weapon will
produce a 3000-rad dose inside a tank within a circle having a
radius of 1 km. A 10-kiloton standard weapon would be
required to produce the same effect.

NATO's short-range missiles

US Army Pershing Ia missile ready for launch.

Pershing 1a

The US Army's primary deep-strike nuclear-armed ballistic missile, now being replaced on a one-for-one basis by the Pershing II, which has greater range. The Pershing Ia's warhead is in fact far larger in yield than its replacement (up to 400 kilotons) reflecting the Pershing II's much greater accuracy. The original Pershing I entered service with the US Army and the German Luftwaffe in 1964, but production switched in 1967 to the Ia model with faster reaction time and air-transportable ground components. The most significant development was the automatic reference system (ARS) which allows this land-mobile missile to be moved to and fired from a previously unsurveyed site.

DESIGNATION: MGM 31A
GUIDANCE: Inertial
PROPULSION: Two-stage, solid propellant
WARHEAD: Nuclear (60-400 kilotons)
LENGTH: 10·5 m
DIAMETER: 1 m
SPEED: Mach 8
RANGE: 160–740 km

Lance

The Lance surface-to-surface missile began development in 1962 and entered service ten years later. It is a dual-capable battlefield missile, with a range of up to 120 km.

It uses inertial guidance and is not terribly accurate, but its basing infrastructure is small and flexible apart from the checks and balances that surround the storage and deployment of forward-based nuclear weapons. The US Army operates the system from a tracked erector-launcher and a loading vehicle carrying two reloads. The crew numbers eight men. Six US Army battalions operate the weapon in Europe with access to around 360 W70/1 and W70/2 nuclear warheads with yield options from 1 to 100 kilotons.

Lance is also compatible with enhanced radiation (neutron) warheads. The primary contractor, Vought, is developing an Improved Lance with three times the range and six times the accuracy of the original missile. Lance is deployed by the US Army, Belgium, the Netherlands, West Germany, Italy, Israel and the United Kingdom, although not of course all in the nuclear role. The British Army of the Rhine deploys one regiment of four batteries, each equipped with three Lances. The total number of UK nuclear-capable Lances is in excess of 60 missiles.

DESIGNATION: MGM-52C
GUIDANCE: Inertial
PROPULSION: Prepacked storable liquid propellant
WARHEAD: Conventional or nuclear (1-100 kilotons options)
LENGTH: 6·14 m
DIAMETER: 56 cm
SPEED: Mach 3
RANGE: 120 km

important symbolically through linking the defence of Europe with the core strategic arsenal of the United States. But when the Soviet Union itself acquired the ability to massively strike the continental United States the stakes were changed.

It became increasingly clear that the 'nuclear umbrella' was shrinking as fast as the United States itself became vulnerable to attack. European NATO had to bow to US pressure to abandon the policy of massive retaliation that would 'punish aggression' by making deep strikes on the Soviet Union and adopt the new policy of 'flexible response', which would offer a defence at the level of violence of the attack. If it came, war would once again be fought at the front line in the heart of Europe and it would move up the rungs of the escalation ladder from rifle bullets to nuclear weapons.

Because of NATO's original nuclear bias, tactical battlefield weapons were already widely distributed in the places that mattered, but, like the strategic balance, were now being matched by Soviet deployments to produce a stalemate at a lower level. There remained the middle rung, the so-called 'Eurostrategic systems', that is, weapons which could reach the Soviet Union from bases in Europe, or alternatively reach European NATO bases from western Russia. It was here that the Soviet Union took the initiative in the mid-1970s by developing and deploying a triple-warhead mobile missile, called the SS-20, a far more formidable deployment than the equivalent nuclear-armed aircraft of USAF Europe based in the United Kingdom. NATO calls its reaction to that initiative 'Theatre Nuclear Force' (TNF) modernization and this is the process that has brought ground-launched cruise and Pershing II missiles to Europe.

The Soviet Union's first nuclear weapons were originally all aimed at Western Europe, which, of course, was as far as they could reach. If 'holding Europe hostage' did not bring strategic parity with the United States, then neither did the short-lived attempt to set up missiles in Cuba in 1963 in an effort to bring the enemy within range.

The Cuba missiles, SS-3s, were first deployed against Western Europe in the late 1950s, followed by SS-4s and 5000-km range SS-5s in the early 1960s. At peak there were 600 fixed launchers pointing west, with 100 more targeted on the Middle East and Southwest Asia. Soviet Frontal Aviation in the 1970s deployed new nuclear-capable aircraft, such as the Su-24 and Tu-22M Backfire, armed with air-to-surface stand-off weapons, while the first-generation ballistic submarines of the *Golf* class were available for use against European targets. Intercontinental SS-11 and later SS-19 missiles were also ranged against European targets to compensate for the transfer of part of the SS-4 and SS-5 force to the Chinese border in 1968.

This remained the situation until 1977 when the new-generation intermediate-range missiles, designated SS-20, began to enter service. Because it

was a 'theatre system' the numbers deployed of this triple warhead weapon were not under discussion in SALT II. The missile is mobile and fitted with three highly accurate and independently targetable warheads. Each SS-20 unit is equipped with a triple warhead reload round. By mid-1983, 315 SS-20s with 945 warheads were deployed, a third facing NATO directly, a third in the Far East and a third in a 'swing zone' near the Urals. The 300-strong SS-4 and SS-5 liquid-fuelled single-warhead IRBM force is being reduced, but not of course at the rate of SS-20 *warhead* deployment.

In a similar fashion, aging battlefield systems such as FROG artillery rockets with a range of 50 km are being replaced by the SS-21 and SS-23 with ranges up to 500 km and a ground-launch cruise missile is reported under development.

The SS-20, in particular, was the weapon that alarmed the West. In addition to the proliferation of warheads, the missile's 'counterforce' ability meant it could knock out NATO's own tactical nuclear stockpile and bases in a first strike, thus eliminating the middle rung of the escalation ladder. There would be no means to make a flexible response in kind—the only response would be to use the core arsenal of the United States, inviting all-out nuclear war, or if the United States held back, nuclear defeat and devastation in Europe.

The existing middle rung of NATO's nuclear response was itself gradually aging and becoming less credible. US Navy Poseidon submarines counted in SALT provide 400 warheads for SACEUR's military targeting, but they are not suited to tactical sniping, nor are they distinct enough from US strategic forces. The same goes for the UK Polaris, while US Navy strike carriers carrying nuclear-armed aircraft are very vulnerable. The predominant NATO theatre long-range forces are manned aircraft and all are stationed in the United Kingdom—170 F-111Es and Fs of USAF Europe. Up to 1983 there were 56 ageing RAF Vulcan B2s, now being replaced by shorter-range Tornados.

This background of gentle obsolescence, coupled with the second round of SALT talks, was highly alarming to some European politicians. Helmut Schmidt, a former Defence Minister and at the time Chancellor of West Germany, made a discreet but influential speech in London in 1977 which contained an implicit message for the Americans. The Soviet Union must be persuaded to reduce the SS-20s facing Europe or it should be matched in kind by theatre nuclear force modernization.

For more than two years after the first SS-20s were deployed the Soviet Union made no offer. When President Brezhnev finally spoke in Berlin in Oct. 1979 he offered too little and too late—too little because the offer to reduce launchers in Europe and not those in the Urals swing zone or in Asia that could be redeployed, still meant that warheads had increased overall, and too late because NATO had in

Soviet short-range missiles

Frog-3/-7 (Free Rocket Over Ground): first-generation battlefield nuclear missiles deployed from the late 1950s onwards. The newest Frog-7, with a range of 60 km and a single warhead of 200 kilotons, dates back to 1965. All Warsaw Pact countries operate them but the warheads are in Soviet custody.

SS-1b (Scud A): A longer-range 150-km battlefield missile introduced in 1957. SS-1c and KY-3 (Scud B and Scud C) are being phased out. Some 140 of these longer-range battlefield missiles were still in service in 1982, 17 years after first being deployed. The range is up to 450 km with a nuclear warhead, for which conventional or chemical munitions can be substituted. Scud is being replaced by the SS-X-23, which has greater range and accuracy.

SS-21: a replacement for the Frog series, with much more sophisticated guidance and greater range. Deployment began in 1978.

SS-12, Scaleboard: a 500- to 900-km-range missile introduced in 1969. It has a single 200-KT warhead. It is being replaced by the SS-22.

SS-22: the replacement for the SS-12, with double the warhead yield. First deployed in 1978, range 1000 km.

SS-23, 'Superscud': a replacement for first-generation short-range missiles. It is dual-capable, has a range of up to 350 km and greater accuracy.

Intermediate-range missiles
SS-4, Sandal, and SS-5, Skean: SS-4 is an intermediate-range missile (2000 km), first deployed in 1959. It is liquid-fuelled, relatively vulnerable and inaccurate. The SS-5 followed it in 1961 and has a similar-sized warhead (1 × 1 megaton) but double the range. Some 275 SS-4s remained in 1982, with a handful of SS-5s, both being withdrawn to be replaced by the SS-20, which has six times the accuracy.

Airborne missiles
While not concentrating on a bomber force to the same degree as the United States, the Soviet Union has developed an array of large-winged stand-off missiles with either nuclear or conventional warheads. An air-launched cruise missile programme approximating to US developments in this direction has been reported.

AS-2, Kipper: first deployed 1960 and primarily an anti-shipping weapon. It has a low kilotonage or conventional warhead.

AS-3, Kangaroo: a megaton-range warhead, with a 650-km range.

AS-4, Kitchen: a kiloton-range warhead, with a 300-km range.

AS-6, Kingfish: first sighted in 1976 on a Tu-16 Badger, this missile employs rocket propulsion with inertial midcourse guidance and radar terminal homing. Its primary carrier was expected to be the Tu-22M Backfire but this aircraft has so far only been reported with the older AS-4. Maximum speed is estimated at Mach 3, with a range of 250 km at low altitude. It has a 200-kiloton warhead. An advanced stand-off weapon with a range of 800 km at Mach 3·5 is reported to be under development (AS-11).

SS-12 *Scaleboard* on its wheeled erector/launcher. Soviet battlefield and intermediate-range nuclear missiles are considered to be less accurate but more destructive than their NATO counterparts. The SS-12 is in the process of being replaced by the more accurate SS-22.

effect already agreed on modernization.

After informal discussions from 1976 onwards the NATO summit of Oct. 1977, held at Bari in Italy, was the first to formally consider TNF modernization, and the Nuclear Planning Group was asked to produce a study. The NPG, first formed in 1963, is NATO's nuclear élite, which includes all member nations of NATO in its councils. It is a small, tight-knit and secretive organization, with an inner circle of about 20 politicians, civil servants and soldiers, and an outer ring of about 150 academics and consultants. Because of European revulsion over the neutron bomb issue in 1976-7, the NPG set up an even tighter group of planners, drawn from their countries' defence and foreign ministries, with direct ministerial access—known originally as Task Force 10 and later as the High Level Group (HLG).

The HLG quickly concluded that NATO did need a new generation of long-range weapons and set out the options on numbers and types. On offer were ground-, air- or sea-launched cruise missiles, a 'stretched' F-111 called the F-111H, a 1600-km ballistic missile called Longbow in early design stage at DARPA and SAMSO, and the Pershing II in a much more advanced state of development. The numbers of total systems recommended ranged from 200 to over 1000.

It was not of course as simple as that. Three factors conspired to ensure that any decision would be fraught with political complications. The first was the scepticism of Europeans and the resurgence of disarmament as a front-line political issue, to be articulated in the streets and in parliament. The second was Soviet use of these sentiments for diplomatic advantage. The third was the perhaps ironic proposition that redress of the imbalance of *Europe*-based nuclear power served to dilute feelings of security.

The problem was that flexible response had always been ambiguous, depending on which side of the Atlantic you stood. For the Americans their forward-based weapons were the second line behind conventional weapons which could be employed 'up the ladder' before the United States was touched. The Europeans, for whom any war was the final disaster, wanted to emphasize how quickly conventional war would turn into a full exchange. The 'war-fighting' qualities of the new weapons fuelled European fears that the United States was planning for a nuclear war confined to Europe.

Thus the HLG had to decide on a policy which both resolved the 'transatlantic' contradiction within NATO and yet was still militarily effective. The most immediately attractive and available systems were the Tomahawk-launched cruise missile (GLCM or 'glickem') and the Pershing II ballistic missile.

Cruise and Pershing

A cruise missile is a pilotless aircraft which flies under its own power through the atmosphere, using wings for lift. In the 1950s and 1960s the United States and the Soviet Union built on German wartime ideas and developed missiles such as the USAF Mace and Matador, the US Navy Regulus and the Soviet Shaddock. They were unwieldly and inaccurate, and the US types were rapidly supplanted by ballistic missiles.

By the early 1970s new technologies opened up the system's potential once again—small, fuel-efficient turbofan engines, advanced guidance technology and lightweight warheads. Cruise was not covered in the original SALT I agreements of 1972 and the more the Soviet Union tried to truncate its development by getting it covered by SALT II, the more its reputation as a wonder weapon grew.

The planners of NATO's theatre nuclear force modernization advanced its merits as a cheap and flexible system and an appropriate land-based and visible response to the SS-20s. It is highly accurate but, because of a flight time of up to three hours, it is not really classifiable as a first-strike weapon.

Its accuracy, however, makes it a powerful military tool and not just a weapon of rationalization in spite of its low speed. While sea-launched cruise missiles were rejected as not being 'politically visible' enough, 'glickems' go to other extremes. To ensure their own 'survivability' GLCM flights are dispersed around the country in heavily armed convoys, with control vehicles receiving command by satellite links (*see* box feature). It made sense, perhaps, to scatter Minuteman ICBM fields over vast desert areas of the American midwest but can the woods and fields of Berkshire or Belgium be used in the same way?

Pershing II is even more problematic. It is a ballistic missile flying 12 times faster than cruise and is very accurate, with a terminal guidance technique which uses radar comparison of the target area with prerecorded information.

Pershing II, therefore, is an even more potent war-fighting weapon than cruise. It could strike Soviet soil six minutes after launch and is thus ideal for targeting military targets which must be dealt with quickly, such as troop formations, mobile command centres, airfields and submarines in port. But its range of 1800 km means that to strike the Soviet Union it would have to be based in West Germany. Faced with this fact, the Federal Republic strongly argued for a 'mix' of both systems, cruise and Pershing, with other countries sharing the burden of forward basing—a condition known as 'non-singularity'.

Although Pershing II was to be based only in West Germany, cruise could go anywhere in European NATO—but where? Britain was already a nuclear power, but Norway and Denmark refused to have nuclear weapons on their soil in peacetime. Turkey and Greece were too unstable, France had withdrawn and Spain was not yet a member. Italy decided to support the scheme, as did Belgium and the Netherlands, but only with extreme reluctance. West Germany led the others in insisting that there should

FROG-7 rockets on their ZIL-135 launch vehicles. A FROG
battalion is integrated into Soviet tank and motor rifle
divisions. The total strength is 18 officers and 138
artillerymen, equipped with armoured transporters and jeeps,
plus two FROG launchers and two reload carriers, each with
three missiles. The wheeled vehicle is highly mobile and can
keep up with an advance. Soviet combat doctrine would place
FROG batteries between 8 and 18 km from the line of contact
in offensive operations and a little further back in the
defensive ones. The guidance principle is very basic:
attendant radar vehicles determine meteorological conditions,
while setting the launcher's elevation and the missile's vanes
will determine the trajectory. The 70-km range FROG 7 is
being replaced by the SS-21, with a range of 120 km.

Raising the nuclear threshold by enhancing conventional defence

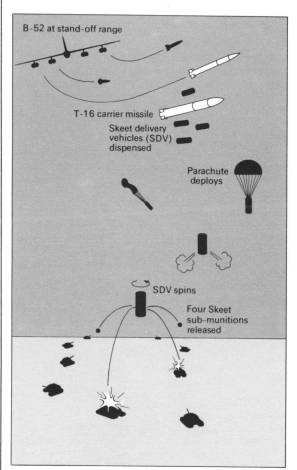

B-52 at stand-off range

T-16 carrier missile

Skeet delivery
vehicles (SDV)
dispensed

Parachute
deploys

SDV spins

Four Skeet
sub-munitions
released

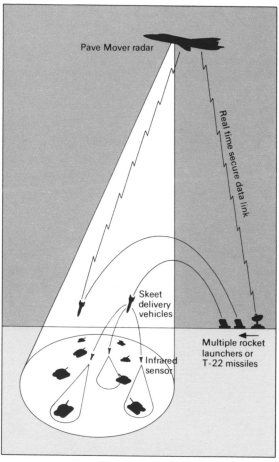

Pave Mover radar

Real time secure data link

Skeet
delivery
vehicles

Infrared
sensor

Multiple rocket
launchers or
T-22 missiles

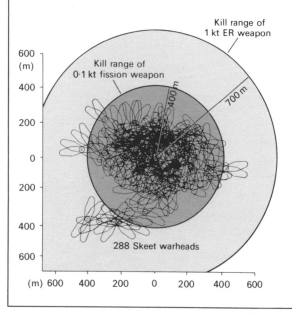

Kill range of
1 kt ER weapon

Kill range of
0·1 kt fission weapon

400 m

700 m

288 Skeet warheads

One of the reasons for the deployment of tactical nuclear weapons is that the threat of their use forces the dispersion of hostile armour to levels which can be handled by conventional forces. In the late 1970s the US Defense Advanced Research Projects Agency (DARPA) began a programme called Assault Breaker to develop the technical means of attacking the second and third wave of echeloned Soviet armour so as to produce the same thinning-out effect at the forward edge of the battle area without resorting to nuclear weapons. Separate USAF and US Army projects were merged in 1982 in the Joint Tactical Missile Programme (JTACMS), which was to act as an air- or ground-launched system, together with the complementary Joint Services Tactical Airborne Radar System (JSTARS). The concept-proving 'Pave Mover' radar, for example, creates a 'radar basket' into which JTACMS missiles will unerringly arrive before dispensing 'smart' sub-munitions.

Weapons like the Avco Skeet home in on a tank's hot exhaust decking and can be dispersed in numbers large enough, with interlocking radar search envelopes, to cover a target area comparable to that covered by a tactical nuclear weapon.

Faced with the threat of NATO's battlefield nuclear weapons, the Soviet Army further developed the wartime tactical doctrine of 'echeloning' its forces in order to thin out in successive waves the potential target presented by a mass army on the move. NATO's forces today are hopeful of holding the line with conventional weapons against the first wave of a Warsaw Pact armoured assault, but there are doubts whether the follow-on formations could be held without recourse to battlefield nuclear weapons and, because of the doctrine of forward defence of Germany, there is little room for regrouping or time for finely tuned decision making. But now new technologies of target acquisition and precision guidance open up the possibility of concentrating devastating force in time and place, with the stopping power of an area nuclear weapon, and of holding the 'follow-on formations' with non-nuclear means.

Four important missions can be identified, at present assigned tactical nuclear solutions, with a range of prototype weapon technologies proposed for their fulfilment. Many of NATO's short-range nuclear blunderbusses at present holding the line could be relegated from a war-fighting to a retaliatory role and the burden of deciding to go nuclear forced on the attacker. The problems of cost are considerable and it would require the political will in NATO both to find the

Vought's improved Lance missile, with far greater range and accuracy than the original Lance, has been tested as a delivery system for anti-armour sub-munitions.

money and move from the doctrine of nuclear first strike as a deterrent to *any* form of attack. Many in NATO, meanwhile, would prefer to see the money spent on reserve stocks of existing conventional weapons.

Four missions with non-nuclear solutions
1/2: Counterair and interdiction
Without air superiority over its own territory NATO has only a few days before the highly competent arm of Soviet Frontal Aviation destroys its reserves and, most important, wipes out nuclear storage and launch systems. The struggle for air superiority is very much about attacking enemy air-bases and aircraft on the ground rather than in aerial combat or by the use of missile barriers and, as matters are, these have to be attacked either by nuclear-armed strike aircraft or by ballistic missiles in order to root out the hardened shelters. More than 70 main operating bases for Warsaw Pact aircraft have been identified and an equivalent number of dispersed operating bases. These could be attacked by cruise or ballistic missiles carrying conventional sub-munitions or by manned aircraft delivering the equivalent runway-cratering and area-denial devices. Similar attacks could be made on fixed interdiction targets, that is, communication choke points or critical command centres far behind the front line.
3: Follow-on formation attack
Attacking *mobile* armoured forces in the second wave requires a large number of weapons systems able to engage targets quickly and surveillance systems able to turn rapidly manoeuvring forces into fixed and designated targets. Sophisticated airborne radars can perform this function while air- or ground-launched missiles provide the delivery platforms for mass anti-armour attack systems. A key development programme here is the US Joint Tactical Missile System (JTACMS), and competing prototypes are designed to carry large numbers of terminally guided sub-munitions.

The JTACMS is designed to be launched from tactical aircraft, strategic bombers or combat vehicles in order to attack armour and concentrated infantry far behind the forward edge of the battle area. Complementary programmes are JSTARS (Joint Target Attack Radar System) and the all-weather Precision Location Strike System, (PLSS), carried by the TR-1 spyplane. In Britain work is proceeding on a project called CASTOR (Corps Airborne Stand-Off Radar), which involves aircraft-, helicopter- and RPV (drone)-mounted surveillance systems. The US army's Aquila drone project is similarly designed to provide target acquisition data for artillery and for such weapons as the Vought MLRS, the Multiple Launch Rocket System now entering US army service.
4: Stopping enemy forces in direct contact
The same technologies apply to stopping armour actually in contact with forward defensive forces. Nuclear artillery can be replaced by multiple-launch rocket systems with ranges of from zero to 30 km, engaging armour with terminally guided sub-munitions. The US Avco Skeet sub-munition, for example, has a seeker which locks on to a tank's hot engine-decking and can be projected in dense clusters, emulating the lethal blast radius of a nuclear artillery shell. Some military analysts are predicting that the development of terminal guided sub-munitions and advanced delivery systems will have the same effect on armoured and mechanized combined arms forces as the machine-gun had on cavalry in 1914.

Nuclear-capable aircraft

A nuclear-capable aircraft is one equipped with the necessary hard points and connections, plus fusing and arming devices, to operate a nuclear-armed missile or a free-fall bomb. This definition can include maritime patrol aircraft, such as the RAF Nimrod or US Navy Orion, comparatively small helicopters carrying antisubmarine depth bombs, big strategic bombers or tactical strike aircraft adaptable for a nuclear role. The Anglo-French Jaguar, for example, originally designed as a 'strike trainer', is nuclear-capable, whereas certain versions of the much larger F-4 Phantom are not. Because so many aircraft are 'dual-capable', they represent the most difficult category of systems to bring into workable arms control agreements. The extreme flexibility of their deployment, whether they are land- or aircraft-carrier based, makes this task even harder. The US Navy and the Royal Navy have long operated nuclear-strike aircraft at sea. The French are beginning to do so, and it can be assumed that the Soviet navy, with its first nuclear-powered fixed-wing aircraft carrier now being built, will be following the same path.

NATO nuclear-capable aircraft
General Dynamics F-111E/F: 156 of these variable-geometry aircraft, with a range of 4700 km, are based in Great Britain under the operational command of USAF Europe. The maximum speed is Mach 2·5 and the weapons load is 28,000 lb of free-fall bombs, ranging in yield from 10 to 300 kilotons. The EF-111 is an extensively modified electronic warfare version designed to provide ECM cover for penetration missions.
F-4 Phantom: a strike fighter being phased out of USAF service in Europe and replaced by F-16s, which are nuclear-capable, although this is not their primary role. The F-4 is also in service in West Germany, Greece and Turkey. The F-16 is in NATO-wide service. The even older F-104 Starfighter has a nuclear capability and serves in Belgium, West Germany, Greece, the Netherlands, Italy and Turkey.

Naval aircraft
A-6E Grumman Intruder: dates back to 1963 but has been extensively developed and remains in production. It is subsonic but can deliver a nuclear weapon in bad weather or at low level. It also serves with the USMC.
A-7 Corsair II: a strike aircraft being phased out and replaced by the McDonnell Douglas F-18 Hornet, which will be dual-capable.
AV-8B Harrier II: more than 330 VTOL strike aircraft capable of nuclear operations will enter service with the US Marine Corps from 1985. The RAF will operate sixty AV-8Bs, designated Harrier GR 5, from 1986. The US Defence Guidance for the period 1984–8 calls on the Marine Corps to 'take the lead in developing a nuclear operations concept for its AV-8B'.

British and French nuclear-capable aircraft
The RAF phased out the last of the V-bombers in a front-line nuclear-strike role in 1982. The broadly equivalent French Mirage IVA will fly on into the 1990s, armed with a new stand-off missile, the ASMP. The Tornado is the key RAF aircraft of the next two decades in air defence (F. Mk 1) and strike role. The Tornado GR 1 is nuclear-capable and can fly very low in bad weather, but does not have such a long-range as the Vulcan. The aging Buccaneer and Jaguar will similarly be relieved of the nuclear strike role

Right: The Sukhoi Su-24 *Fencer*, broadly equivalent to the Tornado and judged to be Soviet Frontal Aviation's most formidable strike aircraft. More than 800 are in service.

Below: Belgian air force F-104 Starfighters, replaced in 1982 by F-16s. F-104s remain in service with the air forces of W. Germany, Greece, Italy, the Netherlands and Turkey.

by the Tornado, when GR 1s are deployed in RAF Germany at Laarbruch and Bruggen. A sizeable in-flight refuelling force is in or is entering service to back up the eventual 220 strike and 165 interceptor Tornados.

The Royal Navy operates the Sea Harrier, whose flexibility of basing was amply demonstrated in the Falklands campaign. The Sea Harrier is nuclear-capable, although this is not its primary role. The Sea Eagle missile, under development as an air-launched conventionally armed anti-shipping missile, has the potential for development into a longer-range air-launched penetration cruise missile for ship or land attack, and could be carried by the Tornado, Buccaneer and Sea Harrier.

Thirty-five aging Mirage IVAs serve with the French Armée de l'Air and 18 will be modified to carry the ASMP stand-off, nuclear air-to-surface weapon in 1986. This weapon will also arm the Mirage 2000N strike fighter operational from 1988, which will replace and supplant the Mirage IIIE. The Armée de l'Air also operates over 100 Jaguar A strike aircraft which, like their RAF counterparts, are nuclear dual-capable.

The Aéronautique Navale operates 71 Super Etendard naval strike fighters, 50 of which are modified to carry AN-52 25-kiloton free-fall bombs or the ASMP, and are deployed on two aircraft carriers. France also emphasizes

in-flight refuelling, with a re-engining programme for the 11 surviving C-135F tankers and a conversion programme for Transall transports.

Soviet nuclear-capable strike aircraft

In the matter of primary long-range theatre nuclear-capable aircraft, with combat radiuses of 100 km or more and the ability to penetrate by flying low in poor weather, the Warsaw Pact at present enjoys a quantitative advantage of 2·5:1. However, as the Tornado enters service this advantage will decrease. Soviet Frontal Aviation's primary attack aircraft are listed below.

Sukhoi Su-7 Fitter A: is being phased out. It also serves with Czechoslovakia and Poland.

Sukhoi Su-17, Su-20 Fitter C-D: 650 are in service, 30 in the Polish air force. It can lift 11,023 lb of bombs, including nuclear weapons or guided ASMs.

MiG 21 Fishbed-L: the strike version of combat aircraft serving in very large numbers. It has a small weapons load.

MiG 27 Flogger D: a single-seat ground-attack aircraft, with 550 in service.

Sukhoi Su-24: a very capable multi-role variable-geometry combat aircraft, the first modern Soviet aircraft designed both for ground attack and to carry a weapons

systems officer. It has a long range, a large weapons load and can cover targets in Britain from East Germany. There are 550 in service.

Medium-range aircraft

Tupolev Tu-16 Badger: more than 500 of this 1950s vintage medium bomber are still in service in nine versions. It has a range of 5000 km and is capable of lifting 19,000 lb of bombs or stand-off air-to-surface missiles.

Tupolev Tu-22 Blinder: the Soviet Union's first supersonic bomber, it has a very restricted range. There are 165 in operation in air force and naval service. Blinder A can carry free-fall bombs, Blinder B carries the AS-4 Kitchen ASM.

Tupolev Tu-22M (Tu-26) Backfire: controversy raged during SALT negotiations about whether Backfire was capable of intercontinental range. After protracted development Backfire B is the primary version, with production of up to 40 a year. Particularly significant is Backfire's potential for carrying advanced air-to-surface missiles aimed against NATO in Europe and, in particular, against the Atlantic replenishment route. Backfire can carry a full range of conventional and nuclear bombs, plus AS-4 and AS-6 ASMs. There are 180 in service.

Above: TF-16 two-seater trainer of the Belgian air force.
F-16s in the strike role can carry two B43, B57 or B61 nuclear
bombs, with yields up to megaton range.

Left: F-111E of United States Air Forces Europe. 150 of these
variable-geometry strike aircraft are based in Britain and, until
the arrival of GLCMs and Pershing II missiles, represented the
only intermediate-range US-controlled nuclear delivery
systems in Europe. F-111s can carry up to six B43 or B61
bombs, with yields from 100-kiloton to megaton range.

be a 'double track' to TNF modernization—rearming while negotiating with the Soviet Union, and this was urged on President Carter by Chancellor Schmidt and Britain's prime minister, James Callaghan, at the Guadelope summit at the end of 1978. Thus, in the spring of 1979 the 'Special Group', later renamed the Special Consultative Group, was set up in NATO to consider TNF modernization as a problem in arms control, to move in parallel with the HLG. When the NATO ministers met again at Homestead AFB, Florida, in April 1979, they agreed to set a deadline for announcing a decision by the end of that year.

The historic decision was announced on Dec. 12, 1979, but without the sought-after united front. The Belgians wanted another six months to decide whether to opt out. The Dutch wanted 18 months to decide whether to opt in. For political reasons the final numbers of weapons and systems were left out of the original communiqué but these were allocated as 108 Pershing IIs and 96 Tomahawk GLCMs to West Germany, 112 GLCMs to Italy, 48 GLCMs to Belgium, 48 GLCMs to the Netherlands, and 160 GLCMs to the United Kingdom (originally scheduled to take 124, but offering to take 36 extra from the German allocation).

The Dec. 1979 decision brought a reaction but not from Moscow. It came from large numbers of politically active Europeans appalled at the prospect of a nuclear war being fought in their homeland. The long-dormant anti-nuclear protest movement reawoke in Europe during 1980 and 1981 and laid claim to a share in the policies of established political parties.

Ten days after the NATO decision, the Soviet Union invaded Afghanistan. President Carter left office a year later, burdened by the Iranian hostage crisis and his Republican rival's accusations of lack of strategic will. The Conservative victors in the May 1979 general election in the United Kingdom were committed both to a replacement for Britain's independent deterrent and to acceptance of GLCMs. Chancellor Schmidt's Socialist party in West Germany was divided on the issue. The new Socialist government in France was firmly committed to a nuclear build-up.

Since the autumn of 1981, parties of the left have lost, or been excluded from, power in countries vital to the TNF decision—Norway, Belgium, West Germany, Denmark, the Netherlands and, in June 1983, the United Kingdom. These parties, now in opposition, encountered the growing political force of the protest movements on the left of the political spectrum. In each case they have undergone a significant change of position on nuclear issues, often opposed to those they held in government—the British Labour Party's unilateral disarmament decision of Oct. 1982 being an obvious example.

The parties in power have also had their problems. The first few months of the Reagan presidency, from Jan. 1981, made it quite clear how different were the transatlantic perceptions of the Soviet threat.

Pershing II

The Pershing II ballistic missile is to be operated by the US army in Europe as part of the NATO theatre force modernization programme. It will be based in Western Germany, from where it can strike targets inside the Soviet Union within a matter of minutes. Although, on published figures, it does not have the range to strike Moscow or SS-20 firing positions east of the Urals, its accuracy and speed (12 times that of a cruise missile) make it a potent war-fighting weapon. The US rationale for its deployment is to couple the nuclear defence of Europe to the strategic deterrent of the United States. It is tactically mobile, on its wheeled erector/launcher, and has a rapid reaction time, increasing its own 'survivability'. The development programme, which has been speeded up under political pressure, has not been trouble-free. In fact, its reliability remains doubtful, but this is not a factor that will be taken into Soviet counterforce equations.

The Pershing II is an evolutionary improvement over its predecessor, the Pershing Ia. It differs in having two solid-propellant propulsion stages, more than doubling its range to 1800 km (Soviet sources claim 2500 km), and a new re-entry vehicle using radar area correlation guidance for greatly improved accuracy. Manning levels are also lower.

The radar-seeker takes over in the last stages of flight at around 50,000 ft, looking down at the target and comparing the video returns with a pre-stored computer image (gleaned from satellite reconnaissance). The results are used to update the inertial guidance system. If the radar makes an error or the data is faulty, the inertial guidance will continue to operate, though with much less accuracy.

This system has demonstrated CEPs as low as 25 m over the full range and, with a yield of 20 kilotons, the missile's counterforce potential is clear. Two sorts of warhead are used, an air-surface burst type of variable yield or an earth-penetrator.

GUIDANCE: Inertial plus radar area correlation
PROPULSION: Two-stage, solid propellant
WARHEAD: Nuclear of variable low yield with two burst options, air-surface or earth-penetrator
LENGTH: 10 m
DIAMETER: 1 m
SPEED: Mach 12 post-boost
RANGE: 1800 km (Soviets claim 2500 km)
ACCURACY: 25 m CEP demonstrated

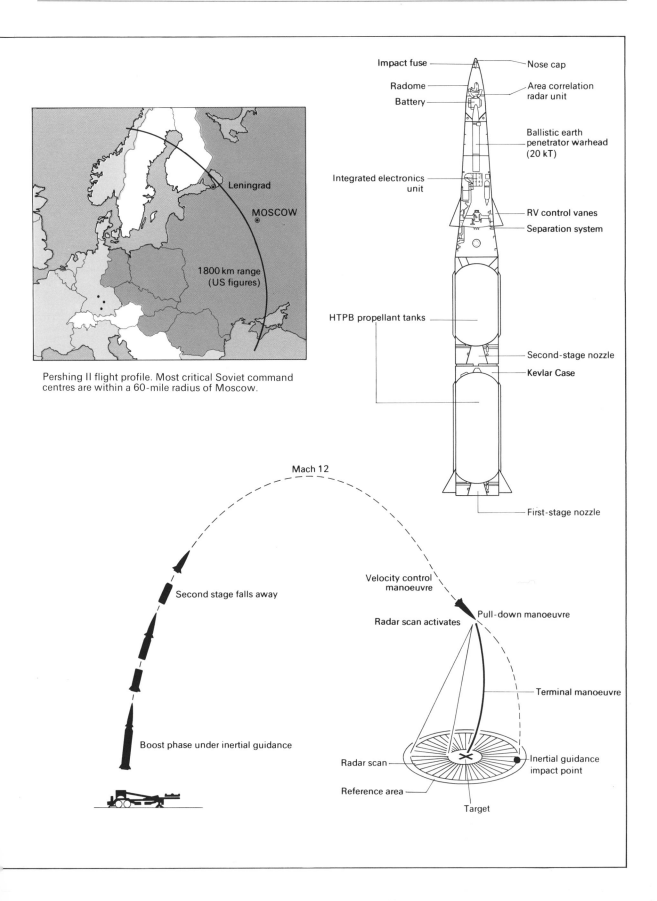

Pershing II flight profile. Most critical Soviet command centres are within a 60-mile radius of Moscow.

Leningrad

MOSCOW

1800 km range
(US figures)

Impact fuse — Nose cap

Radome — Area correlation radar unit

Battery

Ballistic earth penetrator warhead (20 kT)

Integrated electronics unit

RV control vanes

Separation system

HTPB propellant tanks

Second-stage nozzle

Kevlar Case

First-stage nozzle

Mach 12

Second stage falls away

Velocity control manoeuvre

Radar scan activates

Pull-down manoeuvre

Terminal manoeuvre

Boost phase under inertial guidance

Radar scan

Inertial guidance impact point

Reference area

Target

A Pershing II lifts off from its trailer/launcher. From launch in southwest West Germany the warhead could impact on Soviet territory in under 12 minutes.

General Dynamics BGM-109 Tomahawk GLCM

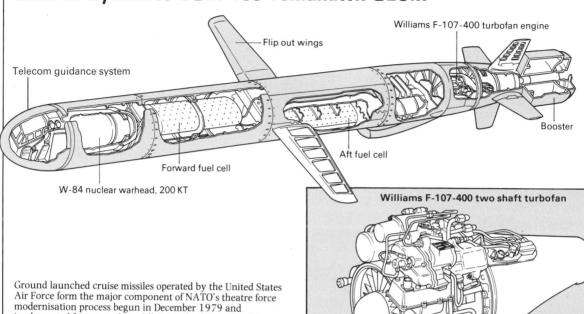

Telecom guidance system

Flip out wings

Williams F-107-400 turbofan engine

Booster

Aft fuel cell

Forward fuel cell

W-84 nuclear warhead, 200 KT

Ground launched cruise missiles operated by the United States Air Force form the major component of NATO's theatre force modernisation process begun in December 1979 and implemented four years later following the failure to achieve mutual reduction in intermediate range land based missiles in Europe through diplomatic negotiation.

General Dynamics is scheduled to make 560 GLCMs, 137 mobile transporter erector launcher (TEL) vehicles and 79 Mobile Launch Centers (LCCs). Each GLCM flight consists of four TELs each carrying four missiles and two LCCs, one primary and one reserve. In peacetime the flights are based in a secure fortified site where a proportion are maintained on quick reaction alert (QRA), the crew ready to move out from their hardened blast proof shelters at a moment's notice. In times of threat or on exercise the units will disperse from their base to remote sites up to 16 km away. Each flight travels in a convoy of 22 vehicles with a total crew of 69, more than half of them heavily !rmed combat soldiers with tactical vehicles. At the site, the troops fan out to protect the vehicles now emplacing. The LCC is hooked up via fibre optic cables to the four TELs while the second LCC is held in reserve.

The LCC can communicate via HF and VHF satellite radio links with USAF headquarters, NATO headquarters and if necessary direct to the National Command Authority in the USA. On receipt of an authorised emergency action message, the operator types in a six digit code into his computer control 'Permissive action link' to allow arming to proceed. Data on launch site and target are then imparted to the missile's guidance system.

The missile housing is elevated to 45 degrees by a hydraulic ram and armoured doors at front and rear are opened. A solid propellant booster blasts the missile out until after five seconds the missile's wings flip out. By fourteen seconds the turbofan has fired and the missile is flying on inertial guidance to the initial timing control point (ITCP).

Length: (with booster 6·4 m (21 ft)
Wing span: 2·6 m (8·6 ft)
Cruise speed: 885 km/h (550 mph)
Range: 2870 km (1400 miles)
Warhead: W-84 nuclear 200 KT

Williams F-107-400 two shaft turbofan

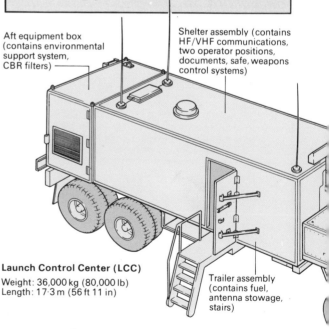

Aft equipment box (contains environmental support system, CBR filters)

Shelter assembly (contains HF/VHF communications, two operator positions, documents, safe, weapons control systems)

Launch Control Center (LCC)
Weight: 36,000 kg (80,000 lb)
Length: 17·3 m (56 ft 11 in)

Trailer assembly (contains fuel, antenna stowage, stairs)

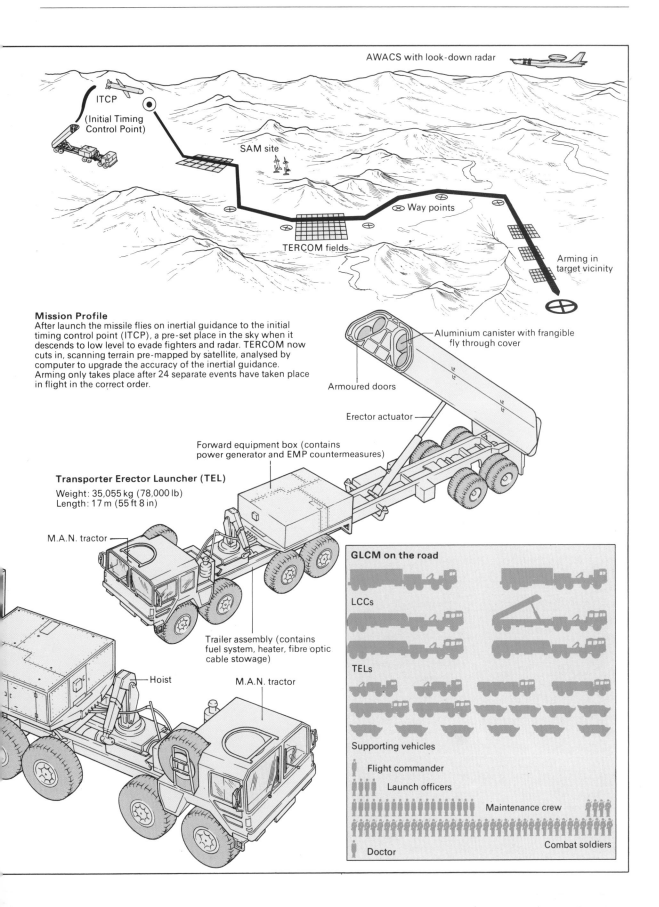

AWACS with look-down radar

ITCP
(Initial Timing
Control Point)

SAM site

Way points

TERCOM fields

Arming in
target vicinity

Mission Profile
After launch the missile flies on inertial guidance to the initial
timing control point (ITCP), a pre-set place in the sky when it
descends to low level to evade fighters and radar. TERCOM now
cuts in, scanning terrain pre-mapped by satellite, analysed by
computer to upgrade the accuracy of the inertial guidance.
Arming only takes place after 24 separate events have taken place
in flight in the correct order.

Aluminium canister with frangible
fly through cover

Armoured doors

Erector actuator

Forward equipment box (contains
power generator and EMP countermeasures)

Transporter Erector Launcher (TEL)
Weight: 35,055 kg (78,000 lb)
Length: 17 m (55 ft 8 in)

M.A.N. tractor

Trailer assembly (contains
fuel system, heater, fibre optic
cable stowage)

Hoist

M.A.N. tractor

GLCM on the road

LCCs

TELs

Supporting vehicles

Flight commander

Launch officers

Maintenance crew

Combat soldiers

Doctor

The trailer erector/launcher vehicle of a ground-launched cruise missile flight.

SS-20

This two-stage solid-fuel missile began deployment in the mid-1970s and was the incentive behind NATO's attempt to match land-based intermediate-range missiles in Europe with the cruise and Pershing II. It has a range of just under 3000 mi. and a triple warhead, with three independently targetable RVs, assessed at 150 kilotons each. A single-warhead version of 1·5 megatons has been reported. The CEP has been stated to be 400 m when the missile was fired from pre-surveyed and prepared positions. The system is mobile, mounted on a launcher/erector, and has equivalent basing versatility to the USAF GLCM.

The missile's range, the level of mobility, the reload potential and the numbers deployed have been points at issue in European arms control talks as the Soviet negotiating position has unfolded. A proposal to move a proportion of the stock of SS-20s back behind the Urals was questioned because of their mobility and uncertainty about their range (they could simply be moved forward again in a time of crisis). Some 351 triple-warhead missiles can be assumed to be deployed, a third facing NATO, a third facing China and Japan, and a third in a 'swing-zone' near the Urals.

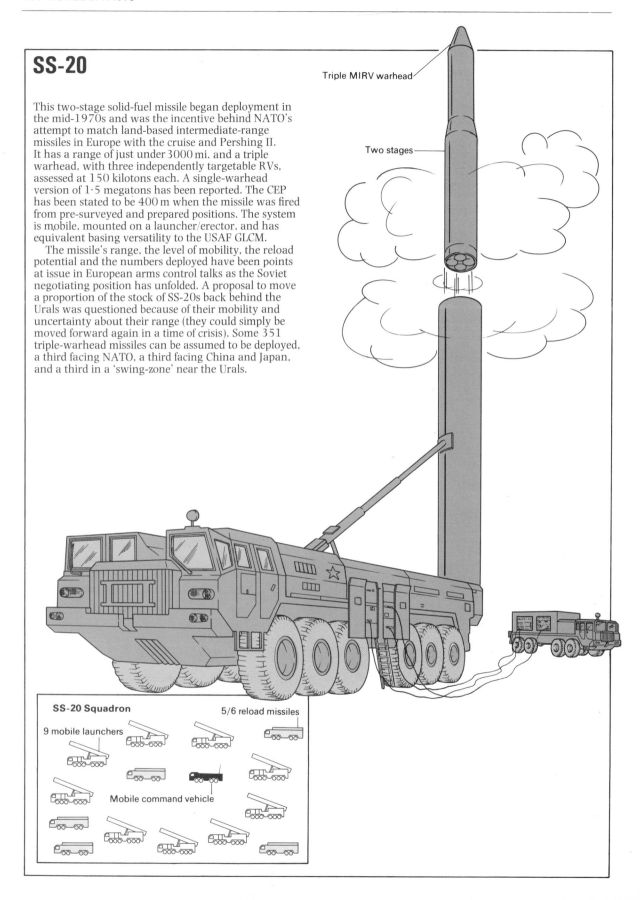

Triple MIRV warhead

Two stages

SS-20 Squadron

9 mobile launchers

5/6 reload missiles

Mobile command vehicle

European countries were interested in moves towards economic co-operation with the Soviet Union, such as the Siberian gas pipeline, not moves towards economic confrontation in the bankrupting arms-race endgame being pursued by the United States. In Oct. 1981 President Reagan made an impromptu speech about a 'nuclear war confined to Europe' and his Secretary of State, Alexander Haig, soon afterwards spoke of 'a nuclear warning shot' in a similar context. More of this apparent American casualness about nuclear war in Europe and the cohesion behind the TNF modernization decision would crumble.

Under frantic prodding from European NATO leaders, the US administration rediscovered the arms-control lane of the 'dual-track' approach. When the 'zero option' was announced by President Reagan in Oct. 1981 (no cruise, no Pershing, no SS-20s) it stole the thunder of the European disarmers—both those in power and those in the mass movements—and of the Soviet Union, which had been offering partial reductions all along. Meanwhile, at the United Nations the foreign ministers of the Soviet Union and the United States agreed to open negotiations on theatre nuclear force reductions in Geneva on Nov. 30, 1981.

The initial Soviet position was spelled out by Brezhnev in a speech on Feb. 3, 1982. He called for a ban on new systems and a freeze on existing weapons, followed by reductions in medium-range missiles and aircraft to 600 systems by 1985 and to 300 by 1990. However, the Soviet Union would not count its mobile systems facing China, insisted on including British and French systems, and excluded large numbers of Soviet nuclear-capable attack aircraft. The number of US theatre nuclear systems this would allow by 1990 would be 37 F-111s.

Both sides went into the Geneva talks, therefore, with a yawning gulf between them—the US zero option which required the Soviet Union to dismantle its complete intermediate-range missile force and the Soviet proposal which required minimal concessions on SS-20s. With power-broking in Geneva bogged down, the emphasis was on Europe-wide political pressure—the United States determined to keep a united front, the Soviet Union determined to impale the western alliance on its own weapons by political pressure.

During the spring of 1982, the Soviet delegation chipped away at support for the 'zero option', mixing conciliatory gestures with new and vague threats. These included putting the United States in an analogous position (which could mean deploying depressed-trajectory SLBMs, able to reach the United States from within the same flight times as Pershing IIs) and adopting a 'launch on warning strategy', again to offset the Pershing IIs' short flight time.

The collapse of Chancellor Schmidt's coalition in West Germany coincided with Brezhnev's final illness at the end of Sept. 1982. The new Soviet leadership under Yuri Andropov took an initiative which further undermined the zero option, with German public opinion as the prize. Towards the end of the autumn round of negotiations, Soviet delegates hinted that a force of 250 SS-20s, with 150 of them targeted on Europe, was a serious possibility. On Dec. 2 came the Andropov offer to the effect that the Soviet Union was prepared to reduce its Europe-based missiles to totals no greater than those of the British and French nuclear force delivery systems (162). Britain and France immediately rejected the idea and NATO did so formally in Feb. 1983, but the Soviet Union had effectively demolished the zero option.

In a speech in May 1983 Andropov went further, declaring that warheads not launchers should be the unit of account and that they would be cut back in step with British or French reductions.

Counting the total British and French nuclear weaponry to see how this offer might work is complicated by recent technological developments. The 64 Polaris missiles of the Royal Navy are phasing in Chevaline front-ends capable of carrying six RVs, not all of which will be nuclear weapons—some will be penaids or dummies. However, the Trident D-5 due in 1990 can carry up to 14 independently targetable RVs and the French will phase in MIRV warhead M-4 SLBMs from the mid-1980s. Thus on the basis of current plans, this option must either block independent French and British action or will have the effect ultimately of greatly multiplying SS-20 or equivalent deployment. It also of course keeps the new generation US systems entirely out of Europe. British and French intransigence on the issue was complete. However, in Sept. 1983, US Vice-President Bush hinted that they would have to be put on the bargaining table 'somewhere along the line'.

The Korean Airliner disaster the same month cut through the delicate web of US-Soviet missile diplomacy. In spite of intense domestic pressure from his supporters on the right President Reagan ruled the incident out of the Geneva talks and went on to tell the UN General Assembly that aircraft would be included in the bargaining as well as missiles. Also, Pershing II with its counterforce potential could be cut, along with cruise, and Soviet missile deployments in Asia would not be automatically matched.

The Soviet answer, with weeks ticking away to the deployment deadline, was the same as before—the US proposal was completely unacceptable. It simply demanded agreement on 'how many Soviet missiles should be reduced and how many American missiles should be deployed'.

The US negotiating position was equally entrenched: 'the Soviets were insisting on retaining a monopoly on intermediate-range missiles against zero for the NATO alliance'. In Nov. 1983 the first GLCMs arrived at RAF Greenham Common and the first Pershing IIs reached West Germany. Immediately the Soviet delegation walked out of the Geneva INF talks, without agreeing on a date for their resumption.

Tactical nuclear weapons at sea

Below: The ASW-SOW (anti-submarine warfare stand-off weapon) system is under development for the US Navy as a replacement for SUBROC and, ultimately, for ASROC on surface warships fitted with vertical-launch systems. The payload can be a conventionally armed homing torpedo or a nuclear depth bomb.

Bottom: Land-based maritime patrol aircraft, such as the US Navy's P-3 Orion and the RAF's Nimrod, seen here, carry nuclear depth bombs. Soviet equivalents are carried by the Tu-20 Bear, Il-38 May and Be-12 Mail flying-boat.

ASW-SOW Motor section

Payload section

Nuclear depth bomb

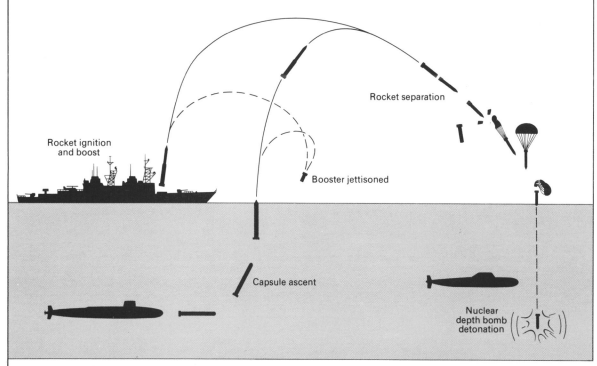

Rocket separation

Rocket ignition and boost

Booster jettisoned

Capsule ascent

Nuclear depth bomb detonation

As tactical nuclear weapons were developed for land warfare, so they evolved in parallel for use at sea, primarily in the specialized role of area air defence and anti-submarine warfare. Because the blast range of an underwater nuclear detonation is several kilometres, the weapon has to be delivered by a stand-off rocket such as ASROC or by aircraft or helicopter. The obsolete US Astor Mk 45 nuclear torpedo was credited with a notional kill rate of 2:0, the target *and* the launching submarine.

The Soviet Navy concentrated from the 1950s on short-range cruise missiles, which may be conventional or nuclear-armed, for attacks on surface vessels and, conceivably, land attack, and only now are comparable systems entering service on US warships.

Anti-submarine weapons
ASROC anti-submarine system
ASROC became operational in 1961 and is still in widespread service aboard US and NATO surface escorts. It is a short-range missile which carries either a Mk 46 homing torpedo or a W44 nuclear depth bomb with a yield of 1 kiloton. Range is between 2 and 10 km.
Subroc (UUM-44A) anti-submarine missile
A primary weapon of US nuclear-powered attack submarines (hunter killers), whose principal targets are enemy submarines themselves. The missile is launched from the submarine's torpedo tubes, breaks surface and flies through the air before re-entering the water in the target area. The W55 nuclear depth-charge it carries then sinks to a predetermined depth before detonation. Estimated lethal radius of the one-kiloton weapon is up to 8 km. Subroc will be replaced by a new system called CASW-SOW (combined anti-submarine warfare stand-off weapon) with alternative nuclear or conventional loads.
US Depth bombs
The US Mks 43, 57, 101 and 104 are nuclear depth bombs of between five and ten-kiloton yield and are designed for launch from maritime patrol aircraft, such as the P-3 Orion or RAF Nimrod, carrier aircraft or from shipborne helicopters.
FRAS-1
Soviet short-range unguided rocket (25 km) deployed aboard *Moskva*-class vessels. Carries a nuclear depth bomb.
SS-N-14 Silex
Soviet anti-submarine warfare system comprising a winged vehicle which can fly up to 55 km under command from the launch ship and deliver either a homing torpedo or a nuclear depth bomb with a yield in the low kiloton range. The system is operational aboard *Krivak*- and *Kara*-class frigates, *Kresta* II and the new *Kirov*-class cruisers.
SS-N-15
Reported to be similar in concept to the US Subroc, the SS-N-15 is a submarine-fired anti-submarine weapon which breaks surface, flies a ballistic path through the air and re-enters the water to deposit a nuclear depth bomb. Range is reported as 35 km but the problems of targeting a submerged submarine in range and bearing must reduce this operationally. The SS-N-15 is reported to arm *Papa*-, *Alfa*-, *Victor III*- and *Tango*-class nuclear-powered attack submarines of the Soviet Navy.
Nuclear mines
The Soviets are known to have deployed fixed nuclear mines with yields of between 5 and 20 kilotons in areas of key strategic interest in both shallow and deep water.

These include choke points through which enemy submarines must pass.
Soviet depth bombs
Nuclear depth bombs are carried by the Tu-20 Bear F, 11-38 *May*, Be-12 *Mail* flying-boats, Ka-25 *Hormone* A, Mi-14 *Haze A* and Ka-32 *Helix A* anti-submarine warfare helicopters.

Anti-ship missiles
US and western navies have been far slower than the Soviets in developing cruise missiles for tactical surface use at sea. The SLCM (sea-launched cruise missile) in its several versions will provide a very wide range of options once it enters service. SLCMs can be launched from submarines or from comparatively small surface ships and the flexibility of basing, plus the fact that SLCMs come in short-range, conventionally-armed, tactical and long-range, nuclear-armed, land-attack versions, blurs previous marked distinctions in classes of nuclear weapon. The tactical anti-ship version has a conventional warhead and uses active radar homing modified from the Harpoon missile.
Soviet naval cruise missiles
SS-N-3 SHADDOCK
Cumbersome and now obsolete surface-to-surface shipborne cruise missile in service since the early 1960s. It arms both nuclear-powered and conventional submarines as well as guided-missile cruisers of the *Kresta I*- and *Kynda*-class. Range has been reported as high as 450 km but in practice is probably nearer 200 km. The standard warhead is believed to be 350 kilotons, while an 800-kiloton strategic land-attack warhead has been reported. The missile is also deployed as a coast defence weapon on ground launchers.
SS-N-7
A cruise missile with a range of 50 km capable of launch from submerged submarines. Warhead reported as a 200-kiloton nuclear weapon.
SS-N-12 SANDBOX
Reported as a replacement for SS-N-3 aboard *Kiev*-class vessels. Presumed to have more sophisticated guidance and be nuclear-armed.
SS-NX-19
Provisional designation applied to the new vertically launched anti-ship missile believed to be deployed on *Kirov*-class nuclear-powered battle cruiser and large, deep-diving *Oscar*-class nuclear-powered cruise missile submarines (SSGN). Range is believed to be up to 500 km, with either a conventional or nuclear warhead. Operational doctrine can involve submarines, surface ships and aircraft operating in concert providing target-acquisition data and mid-course correction for the missiles, which are capable of high supersonic speed (Mach 2·5 has been reported).
SS-NX-21
Provisional designation for reported sea-launched cruise missile akin to US Tomahawk. May already arm *Yankee*-class boats taken off SLBM duties.
Air defence weapons
TERRIER
In service in 1956 but now phasing out from service on cruisers, frigates and carriers. Conventional or nuclear warhead (W45/1, 1 kiloton)
STANDARD SM-2 (ER)
SM-2 version began to enter service in early 1980s and will replace Terrier on existing warships and also arm the Aegis air-defence ships of the *Ticonderoga*-class. Conventional or nuclear warhead (W81, 1 kiloton).

7
The
Nuclear
Defence
of
Great Britain

Great Britain was the third nation in the world to make its own nuclear weapon. In Oct. 1952, at Monte Bello, in Australia, Britain exploded its first experimental atomic device. Making a nuclear bang is comparatively easy for a first-rank industrialized country prepared to spend enough money. Finding relevant, workable delivery systems and a place to put them, both physically, in a small crowded island, and politically, in the context of being at the European end of the NATO alliance, has been Britain's problem ever since.

Britain acquired an operational military capacity to strike the Soviet Union with nuclear weapons soon after the Suez fiasco of 1956. The Defence White Paper of 1957, delivered by Duncan Sandys, seized on the mood of the moment. It scrapped conscription and a mass army, foresaw the demise of manned aircraft and their replacement by missiles, and championed the idea of an independent British nuclear deterrent. It was hoped, on a political level, that possession of nuclear weapons would arrest Britain's decline as a world power, underlined by Suez, or at least allow NATO policy to be developed to best serve British interests.

This could not mean complete independence from the United States. In spite of relative independence in the field of warhead development and manufacture of nuclear materials, in terms of delivery systems Britain was seemingly utterly dependent. Even the home-grown Blue Streak ballistic missile, capable of reaching Moscow from planned silos hewn out of Scottish granite, depended on US designs for its motors and guidance systems. Blue Streak was axed in 1960 when its vulnerability to Soviet counter-attack in its fixed silos became painfully apparent.

The new manned bombers of the V-force, ambitious and sophisticated aircraft although they might be, were merely jet-powered Lancasters in the face of the ever-tightening net of Soviet air defence (*see* page 32), and their bases in eastern Britain were very open to attack. US technology was meanwhile laying out the framework for the triad of missile-armed bombers, land-based missiles and missiles launched from submarines. The first and last of these concepts appeared to suit perceived British needs.

In return Britain had a major bargaining card to play—its proximity to the Soviet Union at a time when US strategic systems, such as B-47 bombers, needed forward operating bases. Strategic Air Command had had an operational headquarters in Britain since 1951. In 1958 it was agreed that Douglas Thor missiles would be deployed, painted with RAF roundels and under dual key control, until Blue Streak was ready, and in Nov. 1960 the US Navy secured an agreement to use Holy Loch as a fleet base for missile-armed submarines. In return Britain would receive the United States' most advanced strategic-delivery system, the Skybolt air-launched ballistic missile, which would take its V-bomber force into the next decade.

But as the United States developed long-range systems, the bargaining power afforded by Britain's geographical position was being eroded. Meanwhile something much more significant had happened—the Soviet Union had developed the means to deliver nuclear weapons on the United States. The latter, which had developed and deployed large numbers of tactical nuclear weapons in Europe to deter a Soviet conventional attack, now realized that this represented a kind of self-made booby trap which could trip an attack on the United States itself. 'Independent' European deterrents, such as those being negotiated by Britain and being demanded by France, simply heightened the risk.

Faced with technical doubts about Skybolt's ability to work at all and aware of the vulnerability of the bases from which the carrier B-52s would operate, in Nov. 1962 the Kennedy administration cancelled the weapon without consultation. The British were stunned. Within a week the prime minister, Harold Macmillan, and President Kennedy met at Nassau in the Bahamas to thrash out a new nuclear deal. Britain got the submarine-launched Polaris in an arrangement under which the United States would provide the missiles and fire-control systems and Britain would provide the submarines (with US help in the propulsion-reactor design) and the missile warheads themselves.

The existence of an independent British nuclear deterrent, therefore, went against the new US strategy, but was heavily dependent on continued US technological co-operation.

The Nassau agreement stated that: 'British forces (which meant the Polaris force) will be used for the purpose of international defence of the Western Alliance in all circumstances.' However, Macmillan ensured the insertion of the vital rider, 'except where HM Government may decide that supreme national interests are at stake.'

That remains the position today. Once again, in the 1980s, Britain is becoming the forward operating base for a US nuclear system and once again has bargained to acquire a new-generation submarine-based delivery system, the Trident II missile.

The first Polaris patrol was made in 1967 and in 1969 nuclear strike responsibilities were formally transferred from Vulcans of RAF Strike Command armed with Blue Steel stand-off bombs to the four nuclear-powered Polaris boats of the Royal Navy. In the late 1960s the Atomic Weapons Research Establishment at Aldermaston began research on a multiple-warhead system, under the code-name 'Antelope', to keep step with developments in Soviet antiballistic missile defence. While this research continued in secret, Harold Wilson's government announced in 1967 that Britain would not seek to acquire the new Poseidon missile from the United States. It was politically embarrassing both as a US missile and as a MIRV system. Edward Heath's government took the same decision, but put more effort into the Antelope project, known now as 'Super Antelope' and, from 1973, as 'Chevaline'.

Chevaline

The existence (and the cost) of Chevaline were revealed to the British public in 1980 by the Secretary of State for Defence, Francis Pym. Chevaline had continued to undergo development through the lifetime of three governments, Conservative, Labour and Conservative again, but knowledge of it was confined to the scientists concerned and a very small number of ministers, civil servants and service chiefs. It was this fact that caused some loud cries of political outrage, rather than the £750 million by which the programme had overrun its (secret) budget.

Pym described the system as a 'very major and comprehensive development of the missile front and also involving changes in the fire control system. The result will not be a MIRVed system. But it includes advanced penetration aids and has the ability to manoeuvre the payload in space.'

After a final series of test launches off Florida and underground tests at the US Atomic Energy Commission site in Nevada, the Chevaline front-end began to replace existing RN Polaris A-3 (now designated Polaris A-3TK) missiles early in 1982. Technical details of Chevaline have not been officially disclosed, but it can be assumed that it is a manoeuvrable post-boost vehicle containing three individual RVs and

able to disperse its 40-kiloton charges over impact points spanning 70 km. Chevaline is not a true MIRV, that is, it cannot attack targets from the same post-boost vehicle but its destructive footprint is bigger and it has greater resistance to nuclear effects and antimissile defences. The Polaris missiles themselves are being fitted with new motors and the four submarines of the *Resolution* class equipped with new navigation and fire-control equipment to sustain their effectiveness until 1990 and the operational advent of Trident.

Trident

Soon after the existence of the Chevaline programme was revealed, the British government announced its intention to acquire a new-generation SLBM to supersede the improved Polaris force within a decade. It would be the Trident C-4, then beginning to enter service with the US Navy, complete with its MIRV system but with British warheads. The capital cost of a four-ship force with 16 missiles each was estimated at £5000 million, at 1980 prices, spread over 15 years. The costs were broken down as 30% for the submarines, built in British yards with British reactors and propulsion but with US fire control. Other weapon systems, such as sonars and tactical self-defence missiles and torpedoes, accounted for 16%, shore facilities 12%, warhead design and construction 30%, and the missiles themselves, bought 'off the

---

Trident warhead proliferation

Britain's submarine-based deterrent mounts 64 Polaris A-3 missiles on four nuclear-powered submarines, not all of which will be operational at one time. The Chevaline front-end improvement programme can be assumed to make at least three warheads available per missile, but they are not independently targetable as in a true MIRV system. Because of pressures to maintain compatibility with US systems, the next-generation SLBM for the Royal Navy will be the much bigger Trident II missile, capable of carrying 14 MIRVs. In theory, at least, the Trident II allows coverage of 896 targets, compared with the present 64.

The French deterrent, apart from the 18 land-based missiles on the Plateau d'Albion near Avignon and the dwindling force of Mirage IV bombers, is based on six submarines, each armed with 16 M-20 single-warhead missiles, and a sixth armed with the new M-4 missile-carrying six MRVs. Five of the boats will move to the M-4 by 1992 and a seventh boat has been authorized, possibly armed with a new missile, the M-5.

By the end of the next decade, therefore, present plans could theoretically leave Britain and France with a total of 2000 nuclear warheads which could be delivered directly on to Soviet territory—896 Trident II warheads, 576 M-4 warheads, 16 M-20s, 18 S-3s and 100 SX mobile IRBMs, with, in addition, over 500 nuclear or dual-capable aircraft. Both Britain and France have an avowed second-strike doctrine of countervalue targeting, France, in particular, structuring its forces so as to be able to inflict

'equivalent punishment' in the context of the nuclear destruction of France.

The crucial decision, already taken, to MIRV the SLBMs, however, goes against these philosophies, since the number of countervalue targets it would bring within coverage only marginally 'improves' the prospect of destroying the Soviet Union as a viable society. Fifty cities contain 40% of the productive capacity. Adding 50 more city targets raises that figure to only 50%.

Royal Navy Fleet Ballistic Missile Submarines
Resolution commissioned 1968
Repulse   1969
Renown   1969
Revenge   1970
Each SSBN carries sixteen Polaris A-3 SLBM converting to A-3TK with MRV warhead. At any time at least one will be undergoing refit.

Below: RAF Jaguar strike aircraft being loaded with conventional bombs. RAF and French Jaguars are adapted to deliver nuclear weapons.

Above: RAF Buccaneer strike aircraft. Originally designed as a carrier-borne nuclear delivery system, the Buccaneer for years provided the RAF with a low-level nuclear strike aircraft. Now being replaced with Tornados, Buccaneers will continue in the maritime strike role with Sea Eagle anti-ship missiles.

Above: British Aerospace Sea Harrier. Unlike its RAF counterpart, the Harrier G.R.3, the Royal Navy's carrier-borne V/STOL aircraft can deliver tactical nuclear weapons, in theory giving the British independent deterrent a global reach. The US Department of Defense has called on the US Marine Corps to develop nuclear attack doctrines with their equivalent Harrier AV-8B aircraft. The RAF will re-equip with this aircraft in the ground role from 1985 onwards.

shelf' from Lockheed, would be 12%. Of the total 70% would be spent in the United Kingdom.

In Sept. 1981, however, President Reagan announced the US administration's intention to go over, in the mid-term, to an entirely new missile for the US SSBN fleet, the D-5 or Trident II, then in the early stages of development with Lockheed's missile division. With the C-4 production line due to be shut down in the mid-1980s, and the Chevaline overrunning its budget, the British government was under great pressure to fall into line with the United States, even though the immensely powerful and accurate new missile would mean rewriting British strategy. It would not be a repeat of the Nassau agreement, when Polaris was acquired at bargain rates, but a very expensive capital-spending programme at the heart of the UK defence budget.

The D-5 is a submarine-launched missile with the range, accuracy and power of a land-based system. It can carry 14 RVs with 150-kiloton yield in the 335- to 475-kiloton range warheads over 11,000 km (6000 mi.) and deliver them with a CEP accuracy of 120 m. The US Navy has developed a manoeuvrable re-entry vehicle (MARV), called the Mk 500, for eventual deployment on the missile.

The D-5's range means that patrols can be mounted from the Indian Ocean or South Atlantic, thus greatly increasing the 'survivability' of the forces, but the power and accuracy of the warheads will deliver for the first time counterforce potential into British hands. This, of course, will greatly multiply the number of warheads available, from 64 missiles with triple non-independently-targetable RVs to 652 silo-busting independently targetable warheads. In 1982 the British government announced that the US base at King's Bay, Georgia, would be UK Trident's technical support base, not Coulport in Scotland. Nuclear warheads would be held and processed in Britain. By now the proportion of the total spent in the United States had reached 45%.

This vast increase in counterforce ability and the breaches of the nuclear non-proliferation treaty would have a dangerously destabilizing influence. This is one reason why at Aldermaston work is proceeding on smaller warheads for the D-5 missile. Under the 1958 Anglo-American agreement for Co-operation on the Uses of Atomic Energy for Mutual Defence Purposes Britain has access to US warhead design and the blueprints for the original Trident I warheads have been made available. These have a yield of 100 kilotons, a third that of the D-5s but still devastating in the context of Britain's preferred countervalue strategy. Revenge which threatens the destruction of cities or, at least, centres of government and not the smashing of concrete missile silos remains the rationale behind Britain's independent deterrent.

There is still the overwhelming problem of cost. Britain has actually achieved what few other NATO governments have been able to do. It has met the commitment agreed by the alliance in 1977 to

increase defence spending in real terms by 3% per annum and, moreover, has done this while real economic performance was slipping and the real cost of weapon procurement was soaring. However, the problems connected with available resources and commitments surfaced in the 1981 defence review. Called the 'Way Forward', it was the most radical reappraisal of Britain's defences in 25 years.

The United Kingdom is committed to four key defence roles—the defence of NATO's central sector through the British Army of the Rhine and RAF Germany, the air defence of the United Kingdom, the maritime defence of the eastern Atlantic, and the independent nuclear deterrent. Something would have to give and this was before the Falklands crisis was on the agenda. The procurement of Trident, unlike Polaris, was to be treated as an integral part of the Royal Navy's budget. It may have represented no more than $3\frac{1}{2}\%$ of the *total* budget, projected over 15 years, but it was nearly 20% of the *equipment* budget, and the absolute sum matched the amount required to come out of the Admiralty's ten-year spending plan on conventional warships and weapons—£7·5 million.

The 1982-3 defence budget was £14·4 billion and the 1983-4 budget was set at £16·4 billion (trimmed within a few days by £230 million). What is happening, however, is that because growth in the overall British economy is static, the defence budget will grow to represent an ever-greater proportion of gross national spending and, of course, government spending as a whole (5·5% of gross national product in 1983-4 and 13% of government spending). The huge expense of Trident, and the fact that it is so early in its development cycle, coupled with the adverse diplomatic impacts of its counterforce multiplication, must mean that Trident is not yet fixed at the centre of British nuclear strategy.

Trident broke the long political consensus on defence more surely even than the deployment of US cruise missiles. The Labour, Liberal and SDP Alliance manifestos for the June 1983 election called for its cancellation. Trident's opponents on the Conservative right say it could break the Anglo-US military axis and when, rather than if, it is cancelled, leave the country shorn of conventional weapons.

Tactical nuclear weapons

A number of tactical nuclear weapon systems are integrated into the British forces. (The operational aspects of tactical nuclear weapons are looked at on page 000.) The Royal Artillery component of the British Army of the Rhine operates over 100 M109 self-propelled guns and 16 M110 203 mm (eight-

Left: Buccaneer with Sea Eagle anti-ship air-to-surface missiles. With a range of 100 km and using a small turbojet, this system could be developed into an air-launched cruise missile as a possible alternative to the UK Trident.

Above: British troops in Germany are fully equipped with individual protection against the effects of nuclear, biological and chemical (NBC) weapons. **Right:** 'Dual key' in action. British and US officers together supervise the mating of a Lance missile warhead.

inch) howitzers, capable of firing US nuclear shells of up to five-kiloton yield. The Royal Artillery also operates a battery of 12 Lance missile-launchers, capable of carrying a US-controlled M234 ten-kiloton yield nuclear warhead over 120 km. The RAF's Jaguar, Buccaneer and Tornado aircraft are capable of carrying nuclear bombs, and the Nimrod maritime reconnaissance aircraft and Sea King helicopters can carry nuclear depth charges. Larger Royal Navy and Royal Fleet Auxiliary ships can operate nuclear depth charges, and a nuclear weapon is being developed for the Sea Harrier. The McDonnell-Douglas AV-8B, destined to be deployed as the Harrier II by the RAF from 1986, will also be nuclear-capable. As the essence of this vertical take-off aircraft is its ability to operate from dispersed clearings in forests or from roads, its use in a nuclear role becomes operationally highly problematic.

8
France,
Superpower
in
Miniature

France is a true nuclear superpower in miniature. It has developed weapons systems almost entirely within its own technological competence and has evolved independent strategies for their use. The commitment to building up the triad of bombers, land- and sea-based strategic missiles, and new tactical weapons continued unbroken under the Socialist administration of François Mitterand, which took office in 1981. In fact, in the 1983 defence budget, the army was to be scaled down by 7% to pay for the very ambitious nuclear programme.

As it stands now the French Force Nucléaire Stratégique (FNS) is a triad—the land-based missile force or Soutien Terre FNS, the long-range bomber force, the Force Aérienne Stratégique (FAS), and the submarine missile fleet, the Force Océanique Stratégique (FOST)—plus the Gendarmerie FNS and Développements et Experimentations which provide respectively, its internal security and technical backup.

The Soutien Terre FNS deploys two squadrons of S3 IRBMs, each carrying a 1·2-megaton single warhead over 3000 km. The squadrons are dispersed in groups of nine bedded in the rock of the Plateau d'Albion, with 140-ton concrete carapaces over each silo, able to withstand the over-pressure of a one-megaton burst less than a kilometre away. There are two fire-control centres, 1500 ft underground, each permanently manned by two officers. Either centre could independently launch all 18 missiles. A mobile missile called SX is under development, with which it is planned to replace the Mirage IV bomber force in the 1990s.

The Force Océanique Stratégique is based on the Ile Longue naval base in Brest Bay and consists of five SSBNs (or SNLE, sousmarin nucléaire lance engins), each able to fire 16 M-20 missiles with a one-megaton warhead and a 3000-km range. The first, *Le Redoubtable*, was launched in 1967, followed by *Le Terrible*, *Le Foudroyant*, *L'Indomptable* and *Le Tonnant* completed in May 1980. Operational patrols normally last for two months, but each submarine has sufficient life support to remain submerged for six months. The five SNLEs in service will be converted to take a new SLBM, called M4, which has a range of over 4000 km and a Chevaline-type warhead. The sixth SNLE now under construction, named *L'Inflexible*, will be the first to take this new missile to sea around 1985. A seventh SNLE, as yet unnamed, is under construction.

The FAS deploys 37 aging Mirage IV long-range bombers, each capable of carrying a single AN-22 free-fall 60-kiloton nuclear weapon, backed up by 11 KC-135 tankers. The KC-135s are being re-engined in step with the US force and 15 of the Mirage IVs will revert to a tactical nuclear role, armed with ASMP stand-off missiles.

France also has the Arme Nucléaire Tactique, five regiments equipped with six Pluton 120-km range battlefield support weapons. These will be replaced in the early 1990s by a new missile called Hades.

Mirage IIIE and Jaguar aircraft of the Armée de l'Air can deliver 25-kiloton AN-52 free-fall bombs, while the two French Navy carriers, *Foch* and *Clemenceau*, emerged from refits in 1981-2 capable of operating Super-Etendard aircraft armed with nuclear weapons.

Existing strike aircraft and new ones, such as the Mirage 2000N, operational from 1988, will operate the ASMP (Air-Sol Moyenne Portée) air-to-ground stand-off missile, which is similar to the US SRAM in concept, with a stand-off range of about 100 km and a 100-kiloton+ warhead. France is also known to be well advanced in the development of enhanced radiation (neutron) weapons and has more than a toehold in launchers and satellite space technology.

France has embarked on an ambitious C^3-upgrade programme, developing a hardened strategic communications system called Ramses (réseau stratégique maille). The so-called Astarte programme mirrors the US TACAMO submarine-aircraft communication systems and will be based on four Transall aircraft operational from 1987.

French missile line-up

SSBS S-3
Two-stage intermediate-range ballistic missile developed by Aérospatiale with a second stage of higher performance than the S-2 which it replaced in 1981-2. The re-entry system features hardening against EMP and penetration aids. Two squadrons of nine missiles each are based on the Plateau d'Albion in southern-central France.
GUIDANCE: Inertial
PROPULSION: two-stage, solid-propellant
WARHEAD: $1 \times 1·2$ megaton
LENGTH: 14 m, DIAMETER: 1·5 m
RANGE: 3000 km

MSBS M-20
Five French SSBNs operational during 1971–80, each carrying 16 M-20 SLBMs (MSBS = Mer-Sol Balistique Stratégique). The M-20 supplanted the earlier M-1 and M-2 missiles and is hardened against EMP. The re-entry vehicle carries penetration aids.
GUIDANCE: Inertial
PROPULSION: Two-stage, solid-propellant
WARHEAD: 1×1 megaton
LENGTH: 10·4 m, DIAMETER: 1·5 m
RANGE: 3000 km
A new-generation SLBM, called M-4, is at the development stage. Range will be 4000 km with 6 MRV warheads. The complete programme, including a sixth SSBN and retrofits, will comprise 96 by 1992.

Pluton
Surface-to-surface short-range battlefield missile in service with five regiments, each with six launchers plus support units. The tracked high mobility launch vehicle is derivative of the AMX-30 tank chassis.
GUIDANCE: Inertial
PROPULSION: Single-stage, solid-propellant
WARHEAD: 25 or 15 kilotons
LENGTH: 7·64 m, DIAMETER: 65 cm
RANGE: 10–120 km

Test launch of the new M4 SLBM from the submerged trials submarine *Le Gymnote*.

KC-135 tanker prepares to fuel a Mirage IV strategic bomber of the French Force Aérienne Stratégique. Also in formation are Mirage IIIs, which are capable of carrying a 15-kiloton tactical nuclear weapon.

The fourth prototype Mirage 2000 destined to be the French
air force's primary combat aircraft from the mid-1980s. The
Mirage 2000N two-seat low-altitude penetration version will
operate a stand-off nuclear weapon.

Dassault Super Etendard carrier strike aircraft. Known
primarily as the carrier of air-launched Exocet missiles and
operational in the Falklands and Gulf wars, the Super
Etendard can carry the AN52 15-kiloton free-fall nuclear
bomb and operate from the carriers, *Foch* and *Clemenceau*.
A nuclear-powered replacement carrier is on order.

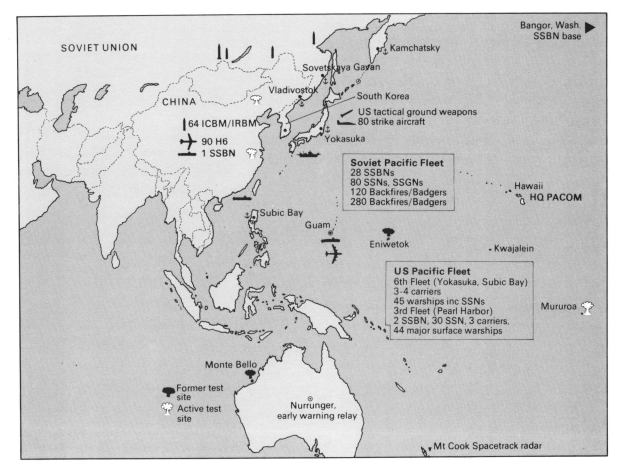

The Nuclear Pacific

In contrast to the massive piling up of nuclear strategic systems by the United States and the Soviet Union, Chinese efforts have been very modest. The People's Liberation Army was built on the doctrine of a 'people's war', emphasizing the ability of mass manpower and defensive morale to overcome technological sophistication. The PLA numbers over $4\frac{1}{2}$ million men, with 'technical' air and naval forces accounting for only a fifth of the total manpower. China, however, has been in the nuclear weapons business for almost 20 years and its efforts are dramatically increasing.

The first nuclear weapon was exploded in 1964, and an operational capability, with a missile, the CSS-1, having a range of more than 1000 km, was reached in 1966. The Second Artillery of the PLA, as the strategic rocket forces are known, is now believed to deploy up to six CSS-3 intercontinental-range missiles, each with a two-megaton warhead. Deployment may have started after a test in 1980 of a new ICBM with a range of 13,000 km and a five-megaton warhead, known in the US reporting system as the CSS-X-4, but its reliability is questionable.

The Chinese Navy has a single *Golf* class diesel-powered missile-firing submarine and in Oct. 1982 test-launched its first primitive SLBM with a 1600 km range. In 1983 construction of a nuclear-powered submarine was reported.

The air force deploys three regiments of B-6 bombers (90 in all), copies of the 1950s vintage Soviet Tu-16. Air defence is provided by a radar system of limited capabilities, a phased array radar complex in western China providing some missile warning capability, and a large number of antiair-craft guns and about 100 SAM units operating CSA-1 (SA-2) missiles. An interceptor force of over 4000 air force and navy fighters is available but they are very largely copies of Soviet aircraft of the 1950s. A new interceptor aircraft, the Shenyang J-8, similar to the Soviet MiG 23, is beginning to enter service and a Mach-2·4 follow-on, called J-12, has been reported.

Great emphasis is laid on civil defence as the strategic component of a people's war, and city evacuation is rigorously rehearsed. Food dumps and grain storage sites are widespread and extensive shelters and tunnels have been built under all the main cities including Peking, Shanghai and Hang-chow, and Huehot in Inner Mongolia.

9
Battle for the High Frontier

On Jan. 27, 1967, a treaty was opened simultaneously in Moscow, Washington and London. After years of long deliberation within the United Nations, the Outer Space Treaty was ready to be signed, binding its signatories to refrain from placing nuclear weapons or 'other weapons of mass destruction' in Earth orbit and to use space and celestial bodies purely for 'peaceful purposes'.

The treaty which entered into force in Oct. 1967 left major loopholes. It excluded weapons that entered space but did not complete a full orbit—meaning ICBMs and the Soviet FOBs 'wrong way round' missile, which was first tested just as the treaty was being ratified, and it allowed interpretation of 'peaceful purposes' as meaning non-aggressive. How could an early-warning satellite, a communication satellite or a reconnaissance satellite have anything other than peaceful purposes?

The key article IV (1) reads 'States parties to the Treaty undertake not to place in orbit around the Earth any objects carrying nuclear weapons or any other kinds of weapons of mass destruction, install such weapons on celestial bodies, or station such weapons in outer space in any other manner'. While this was originally meant to exclude the possibility of nuclear, chemical or biological weapons being placed in orbit, circling the globe and ready to descend on command—it did not necessarily proscribe the placing in orbit of 'tactical' space weapons such as satellites capable of knocking out rival satellites. In 1970 the Soviet Union tested a 'killer-satellite' able to close on a target in orbit and explode next to it. The USAF began testing an anti-satellite missile in 1983.

In the years since the Outer Space Treaty was ratified the United States and the Soviet Union have at least agreed, if nothing else, that these loopholes were there to be exploited.

About three-quarters of the Earth satellites ever launched have been for military purposes. The Soviet Union established a dedicated anti-space defence organization (PKO) in the early 1960s. In Sept. 1982 the USAF set up a separate Space Command (with the motto 'Guardians of the High Frontier') and in 1983 President Reagan announced a long-term shift of technological emphasis away from deterrence and towards space-based strategic defence. Space, therefore, is a fundamentally important military arena and it cannot fail to become more so.

Although satellites are only just becoming weapons-platforms themselves, they are vital to the task of monitoring and controlling the weapons of mass destruction that wait on Earth, predicting their movements and generally providing information about them. For example, intelligence satellites have been instrumental in shifting strategic doctrines away from mutual assured destruction and the targeting of fixed population centres to counterforce strategies based on engaging enemy nuclear forces themselves.

The accuracy on which TERCOM-guided cruise and counterforce-capable submarine-launched missiles depend would again be impossible without space-based systems, while communication satellites are as vital for their command control.

Satellites are not permanent fixtures of the heavens. According to the way they are put into orbit (angle in relation to the Earth, height and speed), the track of their orbit can be shaped for the maximum usefulness according to their mission. Soviet photo-reconnaissance satellites, for example, are placed into low-Earth orbit, fly 12- or 13-day missions, reaching the perigee (the lowest point) of the orbit over the area of maximum interest for a close look. Navigation, communications and early-warning satellites are more permanent features and for this reason are usually placed in geostationary orbits, at an altitude above the Equator and at a velocity where the orbit will match the Earth's rotation. Thus the satellite will 'stand still' in relation to a point on the surface of the Earth.

These networks require careful building, and replacement of the 'space architecture' as their orbits decay or they wear out. This is the military significance of the shuttle, which is able to place systems in orbit and tend them afterwards, and capture or disable rival systems. The Shuttle can carry nearly 30,000 kg and put it into a 180-km orbit. US intelligence sources claim the Soviet Union is building a Shuttle with a 60,000-kg payload and has a heavy lift-launch vehicle that could put 150,000 kg into low orbit.

Military satellites broadly fulfil the following functions. They provide global communications, early warning of long-range attack (and, in the near future, tactical warning of low-level attack), surveillance of events on the ground and at sea, electronic intelligence, weather reconnaissance, and navigational reference and position fixing. Systems operational now, Soviet, US, and other NATO, are examined below according to their type.

Reconnaissance satellites

Lockheed USAF 467 Big Bird
First launched in 1967, this large satellite takes photographs of the Earth's surface using high-resolution Perkins-Elmer cameras and can eject its findings for mid-air 'snatch' recovery. Its orbit takes each Big Bird over every point on the Earth twice in 24 hours. Big Birds are launched at four- to six-monthly intervals and last between 180 to 260 days before their Sun-synchronous orbit decays.

Key Hole KH 11
This is a CIA intelligence-gathering satellite first launched in 1976. It flies in higher orbit than Big Bird, has a life of about one year and transmits images in real time in digital form to ground stations.

Agena D
This is a launcher for a variety of close-look satellite systems, which fly on low orbits and have short lives.

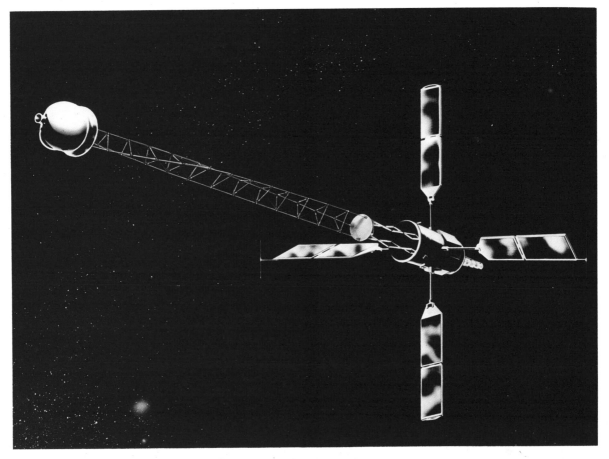

Nova satellite, the first of which was launched in 1981 to give US Navy warships, and especially submarines, a navigational reference point. Three Novas are in the process of replacing the original Transit series.

Cosmos

Soviet reconnaissance satellites have much shorter life-spans than the US Big Birds and KH-11s, somewhere between 10 and 40 days, although a long-life system based on the Salyut space station is being developed. A typical mission was launched from the Soviet centre at Plesetsk, near Leningrad, on Nov. 12, 1980, just as the fledgling US Rapid Deployment Force was conducting its first joint operations with the Egyptian army outside Cairo—a subject of obvious interest to Soviet intelligence.

Twenty-four hours after launch Cosmos 1221 passed over the area to return again, this time scanning a corridor 80 km further west (*see* diagram), bringing its photographic information back to Earth inside the Soviet Union two weeks later. Similar launches were made to monitor events in the South Atlantic during the 1982 Falklands crisis.

Without the equivalent global reach of the US aircraft maritime reconnaissance, satellites of the Cosmos series are used for ocean surveillance. Their radars are usually powered by a small onboard nuclear reactor (which, again, does not break the

letter of the Outer Space Treaty, although these satellites have a habit of crashing earthwards if they go wrong). When the mission has been completed, at heights of around 250 km, the satellite should fire itself into a safe orbit but it does not always do so.

Electronic reconnaissance satellites

Elint (electronic intelligence) is a vital component of electronic warfare. Elint detects and monitors electromagnetic radiation of any kind, generated from any source which might be considered hostile. The information could be the highest secrets of state gleaned by eavesdropping on communication systems, their codes being deciphered by enormously powerful computers. It could be the position of a new radar site or the tactical communications of a formation on the move during manoeuvres. It could be the telemetry transmissions of a new ballistic missile under test. More mundanely, but of very great importance, Elint monitors and records the transmissions of the electronics within a given weapons system. Knowing this 'signature' and the operating frequencies of, say, an anti-ship cruise missile, allows countermeasures to be programmed into the tactical electronic warfare equipment of a warship or aircraft.

An Elint platform is something that takes appropriate equipment to within range of the hostile tions. It could be an aircraft, a remotely piloted vehicle or drone, a vessel such as a trawler or a motor vehicle. The most ambitious and far-reaching Elint platforms are satellites, first deployed by the United States as early as 1962 and by the Soviet Union five years later.

US Elint satellites are usually carried into orbit aboard the large Lockheed Big Birds photographic satellites, while Soviet counterparts use one-off launchers. The US Argus satellites are believed to be able to intercept and retransmit Soviet and Chinese telephonic and radio microwave communications. Early warning rhyolites monitor and transmit data from Soviet and Chinese missile tests.

Communication satellites

US Navy Fleet Satellite Communications Systems (FLSATCOM)
Built by TRW, this consists of five satellites (and one back up), each with 30 speech, teletype channels. They were first launched in Feb. 1978.

Defence satellite Communications Systems Phase II TRW contract for USAF communication systems. This totals at least 16 operational satellites, and was first launched in Nov. 1971. It is used by UK forces on an allocated band width. The phase III system, 'hardened' against EMP and capable of a six-year mission, was first launched in 1982.

LEASAT
Hughes contract for geostationary world-wide communications system based on four large satellites. It was one of the first Shuttle payloads.

SDS 7 Satellite Data System
This is a USAF communications system for strategic bombers in polar regions.

AFSATCOM
This is a Rockwell-managed programme for placing UHF C3 system on US host satellites. The aircraft will be fitted with communications equipment able to receive secure communications through AFSATCOM while in flight.

NATO 3
This consists of three geostationary satellites with a seven-year predicted lifespan, providing high-quality voice communication between US and Europe NATO. Two more are scheduled for launch by 1984.

Skynet
Skynet IIB UK comsat is geostationary above the Seychelles but is approaching the end of its life. British Aerospace have been working on a replacement system since 1981. Skynet IV is scheduled for launch in 1985 aboard Shuttle.

MILSTAR
This is intended as a new-generation service comsat system. It is designed to be highly jam-resistant and able to survive electronic and physical attack.

Molniya 1, 2A and 3
The first of the Molniya (lightning) comsats was launched in 1965, with a highly elliptical orbit, to provide the longest possible communications sessions between Moscow and Vladivostok. Molniyas make two orbits daily, one of which is over the USSR and the other over North America.

The first Soviet synchronous satellite, in the Cosmos series, was placed in equatorial orbit soon afterwards. These experimental launches were followed in 1975 by the start of the Raduga, Molniya 3 and Gorizony series, all put into synchronous orbit. A new class of geostationary multi-purpose communications satellites, known as Volna, was first launched in 1980 and operates in bands allocated for maritime services similar to fleet comsats operated by the United States and NATO. It is assumed that Volna satellites will be positioned over the Atlantic, Indian and Pacific Oceans.

Other satellites
Other satellites also have strategic functions relating to the command and control of nuclear forces, in addition providing intelligence and—very important —navigational reference. The US IMEWS system (Integrated Missile Early Warning Satellites) gives NORAD its first warning (*see* page 000) of hostile ICBM launches from deep within the Soviet Union. Vela satellites, the first of which was launched in 1964, detect and monitor nuclear detonations. A Vela over the South Atlantic detected, in the summer of 1977, the double flash associated with a nuclear explosion, which may have been a nuclear weapon test by South Africa, possibly mounted in an artillery shell.

It is planned to mount much more sophisticated nuclear detonation (nudet) sensors on satellites of the NAVSTAR network in a system called the Integrated Operational Nuclear Detection System (IONDS), which is intended to provide detailed damage assessment both within the United States and within enemy territory during and after an attack. The NAVSTAR programme itself, also known as the Global Positioning System (GPS), has major strategic nuclear implications. It is planned to place 18 satellites around the Earth, distributed around each of three orbits, to form a network able to provide a three-dimensional position reference anywhere on or above the globe, along with precise details of time and velocity. Three atomic clocks accurate to one second over 36,000 years are installed on each satellite.

Not only will NAVSTAR be able to provide precise position references for weapons platforms, such as submarines or aircraft, but also for the weapons themselves such as Trident D-5 missiles in their post-boost phase, or even cruise missiles, relieving them of the need for terrain contour matching. NAVSTAR will also replace the Transit satellites operated by the US Navy, which currently give warships, especially submarines, navigational reference. The first of three Nova satellites was launched in 1981 to provide mid-term replacements for Transit. Weather satellites, launched by the United States and the Soviet Union, also provide operational information for strategic forces.

Star wars
In April 1983 President Reagan made a television broadcast to the American people, reaffirming his commitment to the administration's five-year £2000

billion military spending plan. Towards the end of the speech the President began to speak of an entirely new policy—in his words, 'a vision of the future which offers hope'. The new vision, details of which were delivered almost casually, overturned many fundamental tenets on which doctrines of nuclear deterrence had been built. Reagan called for the threat of retaliation, on which mutual assured destruction depended, to be forsaken. Instead the nation should pursue a defensive strategy based on space systems able to intercept and destroy incoming enemy missiles.

This was not the real importance of the speech, since it is already technically practicable to put weapons systems into orbit. It was the apparent abandoning of MAD that mattered and the new affirmation of faith in the possibility of strategic defence, whether land- or space-based. It was the recognition by strategic theorists on both sides that defensive systems could be as destabilizing and indeed as dangerous as offensive systems that lay behind their virtual abandonment of research efforts after the antiballistic missile treaty of 1972. It was apparent

then that an ABM arms race would be cripplingly expensive and its military efficiency highly doubtful. It was seen that, if one side could be a confident of 'assured survival' while the other was still vulnerable, the compulsion for that side to launch an attack before an ABM defence could confound them would be strong indeed.

The 1972 SALT I ABM Treaty remains the only nuclear arms control agreement still legally in force between the superpowers and, as amended in 1974, it restricts each side to one installation. The United States retired its Safeguard system screening the Minuteman field at Grand Forks, North Dakota, in 1975. The Soviet Galosh system guards Moscow but is unable to deal with MIRV attack.

High Frontier
In his speech Reagan embraced an argument that had been voiced ever more loudly by a group of would-be policy-makers since the last years of the Carter presidency. Under the organizational banner of 'High Frontier' they advanced the concept of space-based strategic defence, which seemed to offer the

Directed-energy weapons

There are two main avenues of research into directed-energy weapons in the United States and, it can be assumed, in the Soviet Union. They are high-energy lasers (HELs) and charged-particle beams (CPBs), while high-power microwaves and means of emulating the electromagnetic pulse (EMP) effects of nuclear detonations are also under investigation. Lasers project a beam of highly concentrated light on a single frequency. Because such a beam travels at the speed of light, a missile travelling at Mach 6 would have moved only nine ft before the beam arrived from 1000 mi. away. Unlike the massless radiation photons that make up a laser beam, charged particles have weight. A particle beam is a stream of highly energized atomic or subatomic particles, such as electrons, protons, hydrogen atoms or ions. A CPB would not be susceptible to diffusion in the atmosphere as laser beams would be, but charged particles would be affected by the earth's magnetic field. Both systems would 'kill' their targets in the same way—by delivering a high concentration of energy, either photons or charged particles, on and into the structure of a missile or hostile satellite. The structure would either melt as the beam's energy spread through it or its electronics would be eviscerated.

Meanwhile laser research is far ahead of that on charged particle beams. US Department of Defense officials estimate the Soviet Union is five years ahead of the United States and could put a laser into space by the mid-1980s. Estimates vary as to when the United States might have a laser in space, with partisans of the scheme quoting 1990 and critics suggesting 2015.

Meanwhile, the individual US armed services have their own high-energy laser programmes and, together with DARPA, have already spent more than $2 billion on research and testing. In 1973 the USAF destroyed a target drone with an HEL and soon afterwards the US Navy brought down a TOW missile with a chemical

laser. These were beams directed from ground installations requiring enormous inputs of power and coolant. The USAF's ALL (Airborne Laser Laboratory), however, based on a Boeing KC-135 airframe, successfully put an operational gas dynamic laser into the air and in 1981 shot down a Sidewinder missile. (The test was judged 75% successful.)

DARPA has a triple-technology programme for developing space-based lasers. The first is for acquisition, pointing and tracking of the target, and is code-named Talon Gold. It is due to be tested on board the shuttle in 1985. The experiment will test a low-power laser, with both high-altitude aircraft and objects in space as targets.

The second technology area is codenamed Project Alpha and is a ground test experiment to prove a high-efficiency infrared chemical laser suitable for use in space. Chemical lasers are considered better than gas dynamic lasers for space basing, because they are smaller, require less cooling and a vacuum (the conditions in space) to operate. The third technology is for super-polished mirrors and precision beam control optics, which are being developed under the name LODE (Large Optics Demonstration Experiment).

In contrast to the multi-service development of lasers the far more challenging technology of particle beams is under single-agency DARPA control. The United States began research in 1958 under a DARPA programme called Seesaw. Although Seesaw was terminated in 1972 the US Navy began in 1974 a CPB research programme called Chair Heritage. This was transferred to DARPA in 1979 and a year later the US Army's CPB programme, called Sipapu, or White Horse, also came under DARPA control. Current funding for CPB research authorized by Congress is running at around $33 million per year, while laser research is commanding over $200 million. Both figures are likely to increase dramatically.

Anti-satellite warfare

As space becomes yet more important as a military arena for satellites bonding together the command, control, communications and intelligence systems of the weapons that wait on earth, antisatellite (ASAT) technology becomes ever more strategically important in parallel. Of the approximately 2300 successful earth-orbital launches since 1957 some two-thirds have been for military purposes. About 70% of worldwide US military communications are routed through space, while the Soviet Union, too, is becoming more dependent. The Soviet Union launches many more military satellites a year than the United States, but they have much shorter lifetimes, especially those used for reconnaissance.

The United States had an ASAT capacity from 1963 to 1975, using nuclear-tipped Army Nike-Zeus missiles from Kwajalein Atoll (1963–4) and USAF Thor missiles (1964–75) from Johnson Island, also in the Pacific, although the use of nuclear warheads in space was prohibited by the Outer Space Treaty of 1967. The Soviet Union began tests of a co-orbital 'hunter-killer' satellite in 1968, using the very large SS-9 *Scarp* booster. Soviet tests continued fitfully during the 1970s, and were discontinued during the abortive US-Soviet ASAT limitation talks of 1978–9. Tests were resumed thereafter but apparently only one, in March 1981, was successful.

However, using the measure that manoeuvring within 1 km of a target satellite is success, 13 out of 20 have fulfilled their mission, although not at the altitudes at which the US early-warning, DSCS and FLSATCOM communication and NAVSTAR satellites operate.

Co-incidentally from 1960 to 1962 the United States ran a prototype co-orbital antisatellite programme, called project SAINT (Satellite Interceptor Inspection and Negation), while the Soviet Union continues to regard the space shuttle as a co-orbital ASAT.

Rumours have long persisted of operational Soviet capacity to knock out satellites with a direct-ascent missile or with ground-based lasers able to blind the sensors of early-warning satellites. Claims have also

Above: The Vought miniature vehicle employs an infrared sensor and eight small telescopes to find its target, with an onboard computer and laser ring gyro for guidance. 56 tiny rockets arranged around its outer shell obey guidance commands and keep the vehicle on a collision course with the target satellite. **Right:** A development US ASAT missile is loaded on to a F-15 at the Boeing Development Center. The missile would be launched at target satellites in low orbit from the top of a zoom climb.

been made of orbiting Soviet battle stations equipped with infrared homing interceptors, capable of destroying multiple spacecraft. The most strident claims have been of laser or particle-beam systems placed aboard spacecraft themselves. The US Department of Defense has reported to Congress that the Soviet Union could launch the first prototype space-based laser by the late 1980s. All this, of course, has served to loosen the political pursestrings on US-directed energy programmes.

The Reagan administration set up a high-powered

United States great geopolitical advantages, and went on to spell out the technical ways and means of achieving it. 'High Frontier' stated their objectives thus: 'Nullify the present and growing threat to the United States and its allies which is posed by Soviet military power—replace the dangerous doctrine of mutual assured destruction with a strategy of assured survival—provide both security and incentive for realizing the enormous industrial and commercial potential of space.'

That is the grand plan and, in spite of grave political and technical doubts, it is now the declared policy of the US government.

The High Frontier plan is set against the time factor and achievable technology. The first step would be a land-based point defence of ballistic missile silos. It would not be a revival of the old Safeguard system, which saw ICBMs being killed in the upper atmosphere by very fast-accelerating nuclear-tipped ABMs,

but would rely on so-called 'swarmjets' of small rockets (about 10,000 in number) that would, literally, put a wall of metal in the path of an incoming warhead and thus destroy it. The next step would be the 'first-generation space-borne defence'. This would entail putting as many as 432 satellites into orbit, each distributed in circular orbits at an altitude of approximately 300 n.mi. Each 'truck' satellite would be able to launch and command 40 'carrier vehicles', equipped with a propulsion module and a kill vehicle —in essence space-borne air-to-air missiles which, through computer prediction, would be able to intercept ICBMs soon after launch. The 'truck' satellites near the Equator would be launched by MX missiles from a base in the Pacific, such as Kwajalein in the Marshall Islands, and, in the language of the High Frontier, a 'geodesic dome' of satellites essentially encompassing the globe would be created, with interlocking 'kill envelopes', through which any

intergovernmental group to study ASAT policy and the President reaffirmed the US commitment to pursue an operational ASAT system in the Oct. 1982 strategic force modernization plan. The 'Star Wars' speech of March 1983 gave much greater emphasis to the military importance of space, although it was not exclusively concerned with the technology of directed energy weapons in the ASAT role but also as antiballistic missile devices.

Meanwhile, the United States has regained an ASAT capacity in the F-15 Eagle and Vought ASAT missile combination and, the Soviet Union would claim, in the shuttle, with its remote manipulation system able to place and retrieve satellites in orbit.

Although it was originally selected as a relatively cheap and quick way to get an ASAT capability, the US Congress has been warned that the air-launched missile system could eventually cost in the 'tens of billions' of dollars, while a test against a space target is scheduled for 1984.

ICBM would pass and be vulnerable to attack.

'Second-generation space defence' is again based on orbiting satellites, but this time mounting laser or beam weapons, or mirrors to reflect laser energy directed up from the ground to strike ICBMs with a focused beam of energy. The study goes on to call for the development of a high-performance 'spaceplane', a manned low-Earth orbit military space station, and increased emphasis on civil defence.

The concept which most caught the President's imagination was that of advanced global missile defence using directed energy weapons and he called on the nation's scientific community to develop such a system.

In the fiscal year 1983-4 the United States planned to spend $1 billion to test the feasibility of such schemes. The Soviet Union was said to be spending five times that amount.

The High Frontier concept was immediately attacked, first because of the destabilizing that would inevitably follow the adoption of a policy of 'assured survival' and, secondly, because of grave technical doubts. How could a space-based particle-beam technology be considered exclusively defensive? If a space-based beam could 'zap' an ICBM as it lifted off why could it not be used itself as a deadly weapon of offence to vapourize a command centre? It was also doubted whether any antimissile system could be made entirely leak-proof. Moreover, if such a thing were attempted, would it not invite the Soviet Union to pile up ever more warheads, cruise missiles and penetration systems, and, in addition, embark on 'tactical' systems to fight it out in space itself with killer satellites? An Earth satellite orbits at 17,000 mph. Even a cloud of tiny ball-bearings strewn in its path would inflict irreparable damage on an extremely expensive military asset, such as a laser-armed 'battlestar'.

Star Wars

1983 was the year that war in space became a great deal nearer reality. President Reagan announced in the spring that his administration had embraced the concept of space-based strategic defence and the US Air Force and US Navy established separate military Space Commands. While the US Department of Defense has articulated a new military space policy and DARPA has pursued its laser technology 'triad' programme, other interested parties have proposed ways of arriving at quick-fix, attainable solutions to the militarization of space and, in particular, defence of the US land-based missile force.

The High Frontier pressure group, for example, proposes short-term defence for Minuteman silos in the shape of 'swarmjet' launchers which would literally put a wall of steel in the face of an incoming RV. (To get round the ABM Treaty they call the concept 'dynamic hardening'.) Medium-term ballistic missile defence might be based on a system of multiple satellites which would be orbited to ensure continuous coverage of Soviet ICBM trajectories, while each satellite would be able to defend itself and each other against ASAT attack. The satellite would act as a 'space fighter', firing non-nuclear missiles to intercept rising ICBMs in their boost phase. Second-generation space defence, it is proposed, should use directed-energy technology, either generating laser energy on board or reflecting it from hardened ground sites as demonstrated in the diagram. Again, hostile ICBMs would be intercepted in the boost phase, before individual RVs had separated and nuclear debris from the destroyed missiles would fall back over the Soviet Union. One proposal would place 24 laser battle stations in orbit in three polar rings of eight weapons, each at an altitude of 1200 km (745 mi.).

In an attack on the United States, six of the stations could handle the land-based missiles, while the rest could concentrate on SLBMs and strategic aircraft. The battle stations would engage ICBMs in the first four minutes of their flight at maximum ranges of 5000 km (3100 mi.). Optical equipment is used for surveillance, acquisition, pointing and tracking and long-range, high-altitude aircraft in the atmosphere would also be vulnerable to laser attack. The battle stations would be hardened against nuclear blast effects and EMP and would use laser weapons to defend themselves against attack.

Two Sprint missiles simultaneously launched from Kwajalein Atoll in the Pacific during 1973 tests while developing the abortive Safeguard anti-ballistic missile system. The ABM test sites on Kwajalein and Johnson Island, in fact, gave the US Army and Air Force an operational ASAT capability from 1964 to 1975, with nuclear-tipped Nike, Zeus and Thor missiles.

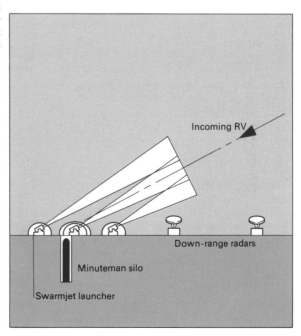

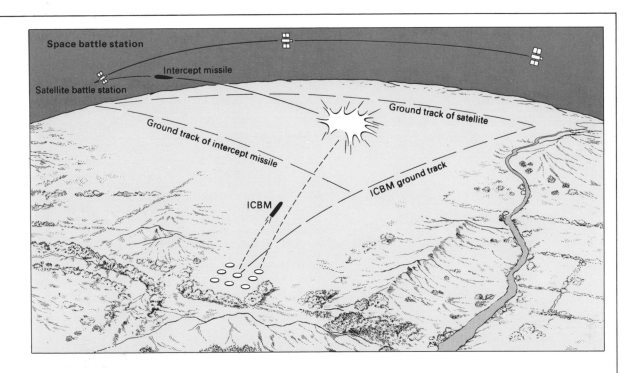

Space battle station

Intercept missile

Satellite battle station

Ground track of satellite

Ground track of intercept missile

ICBM ground track

ICBM

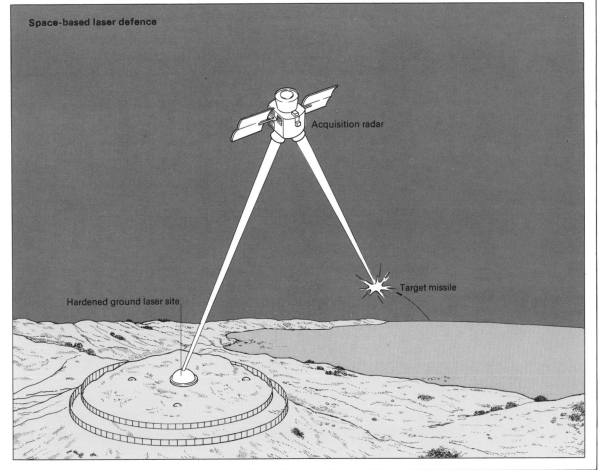

Space-based laser defence

Acquisition radar

Target missile

Hardened ground laser site

Glossary

ABM Anti-ballistic missile
AFAP Artillery-fired atomic projectile
ALBM Air-launched ballistic missile
ALCM Air-launched cruise missile
ASAT Anti-satellite weapon
ASM Air-to-surface missile
ASW Anti-submarine warfare
Attack Submarine A submarine intended primarily to attack enemy warships, shipping or submarines. May be nuclear-powered
AWACS Airborne warning and control aircraft
BMEWS Ballistic missile early warning system (US)
Booster Ballistic missile's first propulsion stage
Bus The post-boost vehicle of a ballistic missile carrying single or multiple warheads and able to manoeuvre independently
C³ Command, control and communications
CD Civil Defence
CEP Circular Error Probable, the radius of a circle into which half the warheads aimed at the circle's centre are predicted to fall
CND Campaign for Nuclear Disarmament (UK)
Cold launch Gas generation to punch a missile out of silo or launch tube. Allows silo to be reused and increases useful throw-weight
Collateral damage Damage inflicted to non-military targets in vicinity of targets, e.g. missile silos
CONUS Continental United States
Counterforce Attacking an opponent's military assets rather than population or industrial centres (countervalue)
Cruise A missile which flies through the atmosphere using wings for lift and under continuous power
DA Dalnaya Aviatsiya, Soviet Long Range Aviation (now relegated to a numbered air force)
DARPA US Defense Advanced Projects Research Agency
Depressed trajectory Flattened ballistic trajectory to reduce radar visibility and warning time of arrival of missile
DEW line Distant early warning line
EMP Electromagnetic pulse. The pulse of intense electromagnetic energy released by a nuclear explosion
ER Enhanced radiation (neutron) weapon which maximizes prompt radiation effects over blast and heat
EUCOM US European Command
Fallout Radiation precipitated medium- and long-term on explosion debris
Flexible response A strategy based on meeting aggression at an appropriate level or place. Replaced massive retaliation
FOBS Fractional Orbital Bombardment System—'wrong way round the globe' semi-orbital weapon
GLCM Ground-launched cruise missile
GPS Global Positioning System
Hardening Passive defensive measures to build in resistance to blast, heat and EMP effects of nuclear weapons
HF High Frequency
ICBM Intercontinental Ballistic Missile (3000–8000 mi. range)
Inertial Guidance Gyroscope-based guidance system for ballistic or cruise missiles. Can be refined by adding systems which use stars (stellar inertial) or ground (TERCOM) as reference
IRBM Intermediate-Range Ballistic Missile (1800–3000 mi. range)
Kiloton (KT) The yield of a nuclear weapon equivalent to 1000 tons of TNT (trinitrotoluene)
Launch on warning Retaliation launched when electronic sensors indicate an attack is inbound.
LCC Launch control centre, component of GLCM convoy
LF Low frequency

MAD Mutual Assured Destruction; also Magnetic Anomaly Detector
MaRV Manoeuvrable Re-entry vehicle
MIRV Multiple independently targetable re-entry vehicle
MRBM Medium-range ballistic missile (600–1000 mi. range)
MRV Multiple re-entry vehicle
MSBS Mer Sol Balistique Stratégique (French SLBM)
MT Megaton, the yield of a nuclear weapon equivalent to 1 million tons of TNT
NCA US National Command Authority
NEACP National Emergency Airborne Command Post
NOP Nuclear Operations Plan—the operational plan for the employment of nuclear weapons by SACEUR
NORAD North American Aerospace Defense Command
Nuclear Free Zone An area in which the manufacture, transport and deployment of nuclear weapons are forbidden
Nuclear Fuel Cycle Uranium ore mining, refining, fuel element fabrication, reprocessing and waste disposal
OTH-B Over-the-Horizon Backscatter Radar. Effective range is about 1800 mi.
Overpressure Blast effects of nuclear weapons affording ability to destroy hardened missile silos
PBW Particle Beam Weapon
Penaid Penetration aid. Electronic countermeasures or dummy RVs carried by a ballistic missile to ensure penetration of ABM defences
Plutonium Separation Reprocessing of spent reactor fuel to separate weapons-grade plutonium
PVO Soviet strategic air defence forces
QRA Quick Reaction Alert
RV Re-entry vehicle
SACEUR Supreme Allied Commander Europe
SAM Surface-to-air missile
SINS Ship's inertial navigation system
SIOP Single Integrated Operational Plan, the United States' contingency plan for strategic retaliatory nuclear warfare. Prepared by Joint Strategic Planning Staff. UK targeting and NATO's NOP are integrated with the SIOP
SLBM Sea-launched ballistic missile
SLCM Sea-launched cruise missile
SNLE Sous marin nucléaire lance engins (French SSBN)
SRAM Short-range attack missile
SS Surface-to-surface
SSBN Nuclear-powered ballistic missile submarine
SSGN Nuclear-powered cruise missile submarine
SSN Nuclear-powered attack submarine
SS-N US code prefix for Soviet sea-launched surface-to-surface missiles
START Strategic Arms Reduction Talks
Stealth US technology programme for reducing heat, optical and radar signature of aircraft and cruise missiles
TEL Transporter erector/launcher component of GLCM convoy
Throw-weight The payload capacity of a ballistic missile including re-entry vehicles of all types (warheads and decoys)
TNF Theatre Nuclear Forces
Tube artillery Howitzers and cannons as opposed to rockets and missiles
UHF Ultra high frequency
Uranium enrichment Process of increasing content of Uranium 235 above that found in natural conditions for use in reactors or nuclear weapons
VVS Soviet air force
Warhead That part of a weapons system containing explosives. Note the distinction between a post-boost vehicle which carries re-entry vehicles and re-entry vehicles which carry warheads

Picture credits
2 Rockwell International, **6** Martin Marietta, **8** MoD via
Defence, **11** ECP Armées via Orbis, **14** Boeing, **16** MoD via
Defence, **22** The Research House, **24** MoD, **26** Flight,
27 (top) Deutsches Museum via Orbis, **27** (bottom) Orbis,
28 General Dynamics, **30** Orbis, **31** Flight, **31** (bottom)
Robert Hunt Library, **32** (top) Robert Hunt Library,
32 (bottom) Flight, **32** Flight, **34** Robert Hunt Library,
46 Flight, **47** US Air Force via Defence, **48** Flight, **48** (top)
Flight, **49** US Army via Flight, **50** Boeing, **52** Flight,
54-5 US Army, **56** Swedish Air Force, **62** US Air Force,
64 Boeing, US Air Force, **65** Boeing, **66** US Air Force,
66 (main picture) US Air Force, **68** (top) Boeing,
68 (bottom) Boeing, **69** Boeing, **70** Lockheed, **71** General
Dynamics, **73** Lockheed, **74** MoD, **78** The Research
House, **79** (top) US Air Force, **79** (bottom) The Research
House, **81** Boeing, **82** Rockwell International, **84** US Air
Force, **86** Boeing, **88** Martin Marietta, **90-91** US Navy via

MARS, **92-3** General Dynamics, **94** (main picture)
McDonnell Douglas, **94** (top) US Navy, **96** Boeing,
98 Boeing, **99** Boeing, **99** (top) General Dynamics,
101 General Electric via Defence, **102** US Air Force,
104 General Dynamics, **105** Rockwell International,
104-5 (main picture) Boeing, **107** US Air Force,
110 Boeing, **119** Defence, **123** MoD via Defence,
128 Defence, **134** MoD, **135** MoD, **136** US Army,
140 Flight, **140** Flight, **143** Vought, **144** (main picture)
Belgian air force via Defence, **145** Flight, **146** General
Dynamics, **147** General Dynamics, **148-9** General
Dynamics, **150** Martin Marietta, **158** Flight, **160** MoD,
164 (main picture) British Aerospace, **164** (bottom) MoD,
165 MoD, **166** British Aerospace, **167** MoD via Defence,
167 MoD via Defence, **168** Defence, **171** Aérospatiale,
171 Aérospatiale, **172** Flight, **174** (top and bottom)
Dassault-Bréguet, **176** US Air Force, **179** RCA, **182** US
Air Force, **183** US Air Force, **184** US Army.